State College

at

Framingham

7500-1-64-932122

ROADS TO DISCOVERY

RALPH E. LAPP

ROADS TO
DISCOVERY

ILLUSTRATED

HARPER & BROTHERS, PUBLISHERS
New York

ROADS TO DISCOVERY

Library of Congress catalog card number: 60-5965

To my son, Christopher Warren

Contents

Acknowledgment

If this book, aimed at the lay reader, especially the young adult, meets its mark it will be because Marguerite Munson has been so helpful. She worked on the manuscript from the viewpoint of a lay person completely innocent of any knowledge about atoms. Having been wrapped up in atomic science for half my life, I knew that it was hopeless for me to recall my early innocence of the atom. Marguerite Munson questioned every word and every idea she could not understand or which she felt would be unclear. It has taken over three years and many alterations in the book—in fact, three complete rewrites—to evolve the present form of *Roads to Discovery*. I hope the reader will enjoy learning about the atom.

RALPH E. LAPP

Arlington, Virginia
September, 1959

ROADS TO DISCOVERY

1⁃

Science: The Great Adventure

SCIENCE is the great adventure of our age. Shortly before the turn of the century this revolutionary new force began attracting men of genius, and in dimly illuminated, poorly equipped laboratories lone scientists or teams of two pursued their researches. But in the quiet dedication of a relatively few scientists there was no promise of the dramatic impact their work was to have upon the world.

In England, in Germany, in France and elsewhere on the Continent scientists like Rutherford, Roentgen, Becquerel and a dozen others were breaking the ground of a new era. They were probing into the innermost secrets of matter, attempting to learn what no man had discovered before. Impelled by keen curiosity and sustained by the deep desire to learn, these men were not content to ask idle questions, to dream or to speculate. They drove home their questions in skillful experiments designed to elicit revealing answers. Often all they got for their trouble was a blurred answer, sometimes even nonsense—or so it seemed. But they persevered, rephrased their questions and tried over and over again. Theirs was a

13

work of endless hours, of forgotten meals and lost sleep.

These early experiments were crude by modern standards but they were thrillingly direct and astonishingly profound. One experiment led to another; a single result triggered a dozen new ideas. Science was on the march at the very time when the elder statesmen of science were mumbling in discontent over the lack of new frontiers for research.

Though some word leaked out from the laboratories to ignite world-wide interest, scientists remained a pitifully small group. In 1905 an unassuming Swiss patent clerk named Einstein jolted his fellow scientists with his conclusions about space and energy. His theory tickled the fancy of newspaper readers, whose reaction was a mixture of awe and amusement. Vaudeville stages resounded with jokes about relativity. Forty years were to pass before the reality of the atom bomb would stun the world with the true meaning of Einstein's work.

The company of devoted scientists pushing back the edges of knowledge with their researches grew very slowly. World War I quickened interest in science when it was realized that the knife of science had two cutting edges, one of which could be turned on man for his own destruction. But the kind of science that was so important—what we call basic or fundamental—seemed of little practical value. There was little reason for society to pay much heed to the small numbers of physicists and chemists and mathematicians who spearheaded this early research into the facts of fundamental science. So the work bumped along at an erratic rate determined mostly by the frequency with which a Rutherford or a Millikan or a Bohr thought of some bright idea.

Bright ideas have a habit of appearing in unexpected places and at unexpected times. However, as the work progressed, more men of high genius were attracted to this vortex of scientific activity. Bright ideas began to pop up with greater frequency. Some truly heretical ideas were put forward which challenged almost everything that scientists had believed before. Supposedly bedrock facts no longer appeared to have their former rigidity. Entirely new concepts of physics found footing. By the late 1920s the scientific community was in ferment.

Bright ideas needed testing. Concepts had to be examined by the crucible test—by devising critical experiments with novel instruments. The period of the Great Depression, the dragging 1930s, was anything but that in science. The numbers of scientists multiplied. Despite hard times, money became available for the laboratories. New instruments such as cyclotrons were invented and things really started to buzz.

These were exciting times. Almost overnight scientists were forced to change their ideas about atoms, the fundamental building blocks of all matter. The discovery of new fundamental entities, such as neutrons and even smaller particles, smashed forever the tidy simplicity of previous pictures of the atom's architecture. Experiments were performed that were to affect the life of every person on earth forever.

At the very time when Hitler was girding his legions and the war drums were beginning to throb throughout Europe, scientists were hard at work on a trail that led to the splitting of the atom. Ironically, it was in the suburbs of Berlin that the discovery took place, late in 1938. Had Hitler had the slightest inkling of the significance of this discovery; had he given his scientists the go-ahead for concerted research in this field, the world today would probably be quite a different place. For the instrument of world conquest was within his reach.

Pure science was submerged by the outbreak of World War II. Professors used to the academic calm of the campus found themselves swept up into the furious whirlwind of defense research. Bright ideas could not be allowed the luxury of months of contemplation; they needed instant action to convert them into something useful for the war effort. Even the wildest ideas were worth considering and exploring—it became important to know what was *not* possible.

University research budgets, formerly measured in hundreds of dollars, mushroomed into million-dollar projects. Research men who had previously led a lone-wolf existence suddenly found themselves in charge of hundreds of people. At the same time the open door of the laboratory, through which ideas and information had formerly flowed freely, was slammed shut and placed under armed guard. Research reports were stamped with a red ink "SECRET" stamp and locked up in thick, steel safes.

In this atmosphere of national urgency scientists put aside their fundamental research, which they loved, to devote full time to applying in a practical way knowledge that had accumulated prior to the outbreak of war. War developments in weapons were pyramided upon the base of many decades of free and unfettered research. One single experimental result —the fact that the uranium atom could be split—was destined to become a two-billion-dollar project employing thousands of scientists and technicians. This project, crowned by the spectacular release of the atom's energy in the A-bomb, would not have been possible had it not been for the patient, seemingly useless work of a handful of scientists, some of whom lived to see their "wild ideas" come true.

The story of the A-bomb is one of the great adventures of civilization. It is a tale of many scientists in many lands, of brilliant breakthroughs and of plodding research. There was much fumbling about with experiments; there were many near-misses that came close, but then went wide of the mark. Again and again men seemed on the very rim of discovery, but they failed to go the one step further—that all-important last step—which distinguishes the work of the true genius. But even the geniuses had their misses; men like Fermi and Einstein were not always right. To the laymen, an Einstein or a Fermi seems a worker of miracles. Fermi took a rather different view of a miracle, claiming that it was merely an event with a probability of less than 10 per cent.

Great adventures in the past have excited the interest of the world and the accounts of voyages into the unknown by Columbus, Da Gama and Magellan make fascinating reading today. It is easy in the imagination to accompany Magellan on his global journeys, to relive his voyages, and experience with him the excitement of his discoveries. The atomic adventure is even more exciting than the voyages of the old explorers, but it is not so easy to follow the uncharted course of the scientists. The scientists in this epic adventure went far into the unknown—where no man had ever trespassed before and into which only the mind of man could inquire. They explored the unseeable, the fathomless void of the atom, the invisible world of the inner atom.

What a challenge this was to man! Here, beyond the fingertips of the scientists, was a new world to conquer. And it was literally beyond their fingertips—a world that could not be felt or seen. Here was the limitless exploration ground of the future. The scientists, the explorers of the twentieth century, needed mental discipline rather than physical courage for their explorations. However, they needed the inner courage to challenge previous conceptions and to strike out in new directions. They had to have courage to believe what they could never see. The invincible weapon that these men possessed was *scientific method*—a thoroughly objective, unprejudiced hunt for truth based upon theory and experiment. Sometimes the abstract mathematical excursions of theory would lead the chase; then experiments would forge out in front, turning up unexpected results to stimulate the development of new theories. But always, inexorably, each man proceeded by acknowledging the work of others and pushing forward. One could never be sure what line of investigation would prove fruitful.

More and more the explorations of science have unrolled a strange and bewildering world inside the atom. The smallness of the subunits, the lesser pieces, of the atom is incredible. Scientists adjust their minds to these tiny dimensions through long association with the results of experiments. They get used to things they can never hope to see, by visualizing the unseen in terms of familiar models. Thus, they picture the atom as a kind of miniature solar system. The heart of the atom, its nucleus, corresponds to our sun; and circling around this nucleus in prescribed orbits, as planets revolve about the sun, are smaller, lighter bodies or particles called electrons. Scientists know that this is a crude picture, but it is a useful educational model for describing something as small as an atom.

Consider the size of the smallest atom. You cannot take an ordinary measurement of it in the way a housewife measures curtains with a yardstick. With a fine micrometer you can measure the diameter of a metal tube to an accuracy of one-thousandth of an inch or less. You can measure the thickness of this page rather easily. But you cannot measure anything much smaller, even with such a fine precision instrument as a micrometer; the rough edges of the micrometer would defeat your measurement. So a scientist who wishes to make more minute measurements must resort to different and more delicate techniques and abandon the "yardstick" approach as too crude.

He may, sometimes, use light rays. We know that infinitesimal particles, like bits of dust, may be magnified with a microscope and thus made visible to the naked eye. But it is important to remember that what makes the magnified particle visible, and therefore measurable, is light. In other words, our information about the size of the magnified bit of dust—or sand, or blood corpuscle, or strand of hair—comes by way of ordinary light, either from the sun or from an electric bulb. With a microscope we substitute an optical measurement for the physical "touch" measurement of the micrometer. Nonetheless, rays of light must also "touch" the bit of dust for us to be able to see its image in the microscope.

There is, however, a limit to measuring the smallness of things with ordinary light rays. This limit is set by the very nature of light itself. Ordinary or visible light, such as comes from the sun or from an incandescent lamp, may be called "white" light. If we pass a beam of this light through a prism of glass, or observe sunlight striking the beveled edge of a plate of glass, we see that the light breaks up into a band of different colors. We call this spread of colors a spectrum. Careful examination of the colors show that they range from red, orange and yellow down through green-blue to violet. The human eye, in short, sees nothing beyond the red at one end or the violet at the other. But this does not mean there is nothing else there; it means that our eyes are not sensitive to other colors. This is an important point to stress, because for us, the world is as we see it, and we see through eyes that are capable of registering only a limited spectrum.

That there are other kinds of light which we can't see at either end of the spectrum is a matter of common experience. The hot coil of an electric stove glows redly and gives off visible light; when the electric current is turned off, the coil soon ceases to glow but we can feel waves of heat coming from it long after it has stopped glowing. We say that there are rays beyond the visible red of the spectrum; more precisely, we call them infrared rays. They cannot be seen by the eye, but they are easily "felt" by the skin. The skin also feels rays, in which the eye cannot see, that lie beyond the violet at the other end of the spectrum; these are the rays that inflict such painful sunburn at the beach.

The spectrum of colors has been the object of study by scientists for many years, a study that has led to much information about the nature of the atom, as we shall see later. Scientists soon discovered that light has a wave nature; that is, that many of its properties can be explained by assuming that light behaves as waves do. A pebble thrown into still water produces a series of waves, which spread out in ever-widening circles. If one takes a photograph of such waves, it is easy to recognize sharp crests or wave peaks. We speak of a wave length as the distance between successive peaks. In addition to water waves, there are sound waves in air, seismic waves in matter, and light waves.

The length of light waves gets progressively shorter as one goes from infrared rays at one end of the spectrum to ultra-violet rays at the other end. The shorter the wave length, the more precise are the measurements that we are able to make with it. Consequently, particles too small to be seen by ordinary white light can sometimes be measured by using an ultra-violet light microscope with its much shorter wave length. The point to be made here is that discernment of tinier and tinier particles requires more and more finely graduated yardsticks.

Can a microscope be made more powerful than the ultra-violet light type? The answer is yes, but we shall need something that has a still shorter wave length. For this, let us consider those tiny packets of electrical energy—the smallest carrier of electrical charge—the electrons. Electrons are infinitesimal bits of negatively charged matter. Some, which might be called captive electrons, are a component of all atoms; countless others—free electrons—swarm throughout space and serve modern man in a host of ways: in electrical current, in radio tubes, in storage batteries, in hearing aids, and in television tubes. In TV tubes the electrons are emitted from a hot tungsten filament and are hurled forward in the big evacuated glass TV tube by means of the high voltage inside the set. As they hit the fluorescent screen, each one produces a tiny flash or light (scintillation). These electrons behave as little projectiles or bullets; their tiny size is indicated by the fact that in a fleeting millionth of one second a billion, billion electrons will dart through the TV tube.

At first thought, electrons might seem useless in a microscope since they are particles, not waves. However, it is known that solid particles exhibit wave properties. Ordinarily, when we deal with large objects, such wave properties are not important or even verifiable. But with tiny specks of matter the wave nature of the particles becomes important. We know that electrons are exceedingly tiny and do behave as waves. We can thus describe a beam of electrons as characterized by a certain wave length. This wave length depends upon the speed of the electrons; the higher the speed, the shorter the wave length. Even only moderately fast electrons have wave lengths shorter than those of ultraviolet rays.

Electron microscopes have been so highly developed that they are capable of magnifying objects a hundred thousand times. Even the rodlike and spherical viruses can be clearly photographed with an electron microscope. One may also photograph the threadlike, striated chromosomes in sex cells. These banded chromosomes are what determine heredity in plants, animals and humans. Yet this tiny chromosome is itself a vast complex of a thousand smaller subunits, which we call genes. Genes are not visible even under the best magnification, but we know that they must exist because of many experiments that geneticists have performed. But even the invisible gene is made up of still smaller and more elementary units, such as proteins—the vital stuff of life.

Chemists who study the nature of proteins have discovered that they are themselves highly complex substances. The human body contains thousands of different kinds of proteins, each of which has a distinctive structure and a special role to play in the functioning of our cells. Proteins are actually colossal molecules of great complexity, and there are subunits called amino acids inside the protein structure. The molecule of beef insulin, for instance, is made up of fifty-one amino acid groups, and each amino acid is itself a complex of still smaller units called atoms. The hemoglobin molecule (red blood cell), for instance, is made up of almost ten thousand individual atoms.

This is about as far as we shall go at this point in delving into the smallness of things. Later on we shall look closer at the atom, estimate its size, and then see what lies inside it. If the sequence of smaller and smaller units that we have followed is at first hard to comprehend, one reason is not that these things are so small but that we ourselves are so big, compared with atoms, and are not used to this microscopic world. One way of putting things into perspective is to go in an airplane high above the earth and look down upon a metropolitan area. In an aerial view of the region stretching from the southern edge of Washington, D.C., to Mt. Vernon, where George Washington lived, from a vantage point of ten miles up in the air, one can make out the outline of the city blocks in Alexandria. Individual city blocks are visible but the houses cannot be distinguished, although we know of course that they are there. And in each house there are many rooms, many people and many objects. A modern city is a compact mass of usually well-ordered things. In the same way a magnified view of the world beyond our fingertips and beyond seeing is a complex, beautifully arranged organization. It is the purpose of this book to describe what the scientists "see" in this subminiature world and to explain something of the exquisite harmony that prevails there.

2.

Dr. Roentgen Discovers
X - Rays

IF we look back into history to trace the beginnings of the Atomic Age, we may start the story with an experiment performed by a tall, scholarly, bearded professor of physics in the Bavarian town of Würzburg late in the year 1895.

Dr. Wilhelm Konrad Roentgen was fifty years old when he turned his attention to some problems that had puzzled him for some time. He had become curious about what took place when electricity was sent through a sealed glass tube from which most of the air had been pumped. Technically, you could say he had been experimenting with the passage of electricity through gas, since air—oxygen and nitrogen—is a gas. For this purpose he used a pear-shaped, rather large glass vessel, called a Lenard tube, into which he had sealed two metal electrodes, or conductors of electricity. To these electrodes (one, the cathode, is positive; the other, the anode, negative) he attached wires from a high-voltage machine. Roentgen was not the first to experiment with such tubes; in fact, dozens of scientists had observed the passage of electrical current through similar tubes for many years preceding the experiment we shall describe. From their work and his own observations, Roentgen knew that if he connected his tube to a vacuum pump and produced a poor vacuum—that is, removed all but one-thousandth of the original air—the tube would be filled with a diffuse and rather pretty pink glow when electricity was sent through it. At lower pressures the pink glow would vanish, to be replaced by a thin bluish glow stretching from one metal electrode to the other. Both the pink and the blue glow were caused by the collision of the electrons passing through the tube with the rarefied air remaining in it. At still lower pressures even the blue light vanished, since there was not enough air (i.e., gas atoms) left for the fast-moving electrons to collide with.

But even when as much air as possible had been pumped out, the passage of electricity through the tube still produced an interesting effect: the fused end of the glass tube would give off a greenish, rather ghostly light. This green fluorescence was caused by the impact of the speedy electrons upon the glass.

One day, now famous in history, November 8, 1895—Friday afternoon, to be precise—Roentgen, having dined with his wife, hurried back to the laboratory to try another experiment. Roentgen worked alone in a ground-floor room whose windows looked out upon an attractive garden. In a cabinet he had a collection of variously shaped discharge tubes, as he called them. Others called them Hittorf, Lenard or Crookes tubes, after the scientists who had designed them. Roentgen had been experimenting with a Lenard tube which was equipped with an aluminum window so thin that the fast-moving electrons, or cathode rays, could pass through it into the air. It was the study of these rays that had intrigued him. This particular evening, however, he took a thick-walled glass discharge tube with a fused glass window through which the cathode rays could not pass, and wrapped it in a mantle of cardboard, sealing the edges so that no light from the tube would leak out.

Then he drew the shades on the windows, making sure that the room was completely dark. When his eyes became accustomed to the blackness, from long habit Roentgen found and threw the switch of his high-voltage machine. No light escaped from the covered discharge tube. Suddenly his eye was caught by a ghostly flickering of greenish light about three feet away from the tube. It was strange. Almost instinctively he flipped the switch to his apparatus. The light disappeared. But it promptly glowed again when he once more applied the high voltage to the tube. Whatever the glow was, clearly it must be caused by the apparatus. Roentgen struck a match and looked for the source of the flickering light. It was coming from a piece of cardboard that he had coated with crystals of a chemical called barium platinocyanide, which he had used in a previous experiment. How odd that it should glow so far away from the discharge tube.

Holding the piece of cardboard closer to his apparatus, the scientist observed that it now glowed brilliantly. Obviously something—some ray—must be coming from the tube and causing the crystals to sparkle. A less skilled observer might have passed over the effect, but Roentgen realized that the rays, whatever they might be, were most peculiar. For they penetrated not only the glass walls of the tube and the cardboard in which it was encased, but even through the thickness of a book which he placed between his tube and the crystal screen.

Roentgen's interest was greatly stimulated by the mystery of the strange invisible rays that were produced inside his glass tube, that could penetrate solid matter and cause barium crystals to scintillate, or fluoresce. Needing a name for these unknown rays, he aptly dubbed them "X-rays."

He now became completely engrossed in his investigation of X-rays. Working alone, he performed a series of systematic experiments, and by the end of the year he had learned a great deal about them. He found that they affected photographic film, causing it to turn black when it was developed. He wrapped a piece of photographic film in black paper, to protect it from light, placed a metal key on the packet and then exposed it to X-rays. When he developed the film, he found the key had left its image there. The X-rays had blackened the film all around it, but where the key had lain, the film was untouched by the rays. They had been stopped or absorbed by the heavy metal of the key.

Fascinated with his X-ray photograph of the key, Roentgen took his favorite hunting gun and made an X-ray picture of that. The details of the metal parts showed up clearly. This experiment was the forerunner of industrial radiography, in which X-rays are used to examine structures and machinery for internal flaws.

Not content with photographing inanimate objects, Roentgen asked his wife to help him in an experiment. He placed a paper-wrapped photographic film beneath her hand and exposed it for fifteen minutes to X-rays from his tube. When the film was developed the bones of her fingers showed up clearly in the faint outline of her entire hand, the bones having stopped more of the rays than had the fleshy part of the hand. Her wedding ring stood out starkly where the X-rays had been completely absorbed by the heavy gold. This experiment initiated a whole new era in medical diagnosis—the science of roentgenology or radiology.

Roentgen made another observation of even greater importance to human welfare. Using his cardboard covered with barium crystals as a kind of viewing screen, he placed it close to his X-ray tube, and holding his hand between the tube and screen was able to observe on the screen a shadow outline of the bones. He could see the image of his finger bones move when he wiggled his fingers.

In his own words, "If the hand be held before the fluorescent screen, the shadow shows the bones darkly, with only faint outlines of the surrounding tissues." The explanation of this is that, as we have seen, barium and certain other crystals are excited to emit flashes of light when struck by X-rays. What happens is that they are absorbing energy from the X-rays and giving it out as visible radiation. Naturally, the crystal screen glows more or less brightly according to the strength of the rays hitting it; dark shadows are produced where more of the X-rays are stopped in the denser substance of the bones, and lighter patches of greenish-blue tone show up where they are less absorbed by the flesh. Roentgen's fluorescent screen became the modern X-ray fluoroscope, which is such a valuable tool in the examination of the human body.

The practical applications of X-rays are important, but Roentgen was more concerned about the physics of what he had discovered. When he closeted himself in his laboratory he became so absorbed with trying to understand all he could about X-rays that he shut the world out. He even forgot to eat and sometimes slept in his laboratory. By late December he had assembled his data and prepared a paper for the Physical Medical Society of Würzburg. The paper, titled "On a New Kind of Rays," presented his results in a series of seventeen statements on the properties of X-rays. No scientific discovery of comparable value had ever been so completely the work of one man.

This written communication, dated December 28, 1895, did not immediately reach the world outside of Würzburg. But on New Year's Day, Roentgen sent copies of his X-ray photos to seven of his colleagues. A friend of one of the recipients told a newsman about the discovery, and on January 5 the Vienna Presse broke the story of X-rays. It was a sensational story and overnight the solemn discoverer of X-rays was world-famous. It was the last thing that he desired, for throughout his life he shunned publicity. In fact, he gave only two public lectures about X-rays.

A number of other scientists must have been shocked to learn of Roentgen's discovery. There is no question that other researchers had, without being aware of it, produced X-rays in apparatus not very different from Roentgen's. The great English scientist, Sir William Crookes, had worked with similar tubes and had found, much to his annoyance, that photographic film kept in the laboratory became fogged. He returned package after package of the film, complaining that it was defective. One may speculate that if Sir William had carelessly left a house key on one of the film packages he might today be celebrated as the discoverer of X-rays.

It would be a mistake to think that Roentgen's discovery did not depend upon the work of others. Roughly two decades before his discovery of X-rays, the physicist Johann Hittorf had experimented with similar discharge tubes. It was research by the Hungarian Philipp Lenard that caused Roentgen to become interested in the greenish fluorescence on the glass window or walls of his tube.

Once Roentgen's discovery was announced, scientists all over the world were quick to recognize its importance. However, nonscientists were alarmed. For example, the British morning newspaper the *Standard*, featured a news story on X-rays in its January 7, 1896, edition. People did not understand the nature of the new rays and became frightened. One city actually passed a law forbidding the use of "X-ray glasses" on the grounds that they would invade a person's privacy.

Medical men were not dismayed that X-rays could "look inside" the human body. They welcomed the discovery as a powerful new tool for medical diagnosis. So far as is known, the first useful application of X-rays in the United States took place on February 3, 1896, when two Dartmouth College professors took an X-ray photograph of a young man's arm to reveal a fracture. The X-ray tube they used produced such weak X-rays that it took an exposure of twenty minutes to make the picture.

Today the use of X-rays enriches our lives because of the valuable assistance it gives the doctor in analyzing a patient's

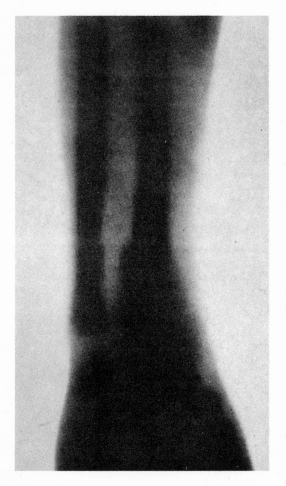

1. First known X-ray photograph of a bone fracture. (Dartmouth Alumni Magazine)

ills. This fact is so obvious that there is no need to expand upon the subject. Our interest here is not so much in applications of science as in the nature of the scientific world. We are interested in learning about the scientist, how he pursues his science and what this has revealed to us about the structure of our universe.

Roentgen, himself, was completely immersed in his research. Once he recognized that X-rays were a new discovery and different from any other rays known at the time, he asked himself all sorts of questions. How penetrating are the rays? Can they be focused like rays of light in a lens? Are the X-rays affected by the power of a strong magnet? How are the X-rays produced? What happens when an X-ray is stopped in a piece of lead? Are X-rays all the same or do they depend in some way upon the voltage applied to the tube? Does the metal forming the electrodes in the tube affect the production of X-rays?

To get the answers, Roentgen converted his questions into carefully thought-out experiments. Wanting to know to what extent different elements absorb X-rays, he interposed various thicknesses of platinum, lead, zinc and aluminum foil between the X-ray tube and a photographic plate. He then estimated the amounts of material required to produce the same blackening effect upon the film. In this way he found that heavy elements soaked up from ten to twenty times more X-rays than very light elements. Lead is a common, cheap, as well as heavy element and for this reason it is an excellent choice as a shield against X-rays. Roentgen found that a sheet of lead only 0.06 inch thick absorbed practically all the X-rays generated in his tube.

Roentgen did not have a high-voltage machine capable of producing, say, 100,000 volts across his tube. He could not therefore investigate the properties of such high-energy X-rays. Had he been able to do so he would have been interested by the fact that the 100,000-volt X-rays are very penetrating.

We call such X-rays "hard," whereas the rays from Roentgen's early apparatus we call "soft." This way of naming the quality of the rays refers to their penetrating power. X-rays produced in the small, portable unit that dentists use usually run about 65,000 volts. However, X-rays of two and three times this voltage are common in medical practice. (Voltage refers to the speed with which electrons fly through a vacuum.)

Among the many things that Roentgen wanted to know was what happened when his rays were absorbed in matter. For example, did they produce heat? The German scientist performed an experiment to measure this effect and concluded: "I have not been able to show experimentally that the X-rays give rise to any calorific [heat] effects." Note the language that Roentgen used. He did not assert that no heat was produced; he simply stated that his experiment did not detect it. This is the scientist's precise way of communicating his results. Had Roentgen possessed the highly sensitive instruments that are made today, he could have verified that heat is, in fact, the ultimate end product when X-rays are stopped in matter. His instruments, however, were too crude to measure this effect.

One of the things that fascinated Roentgen about the behavior of X-rays was their ability to make air conduct electricity. He knew that when he took an insulated jar—that is, a container with a central electrode well insulated from the walls—and applied an electrical charge to the center wire, the charge remained undiminished for days. However, he found that when he irradiated the container with X-rays the electrical charge leaked off the wire. This could be explained by assuming that X-rays somehow or other changed the nature of the smallest entities (atoms) of air so that they formed a conducting path between the wire and the wall of the jar. This result stimulated him to study the "electrified air." He did a number of ingenious experiments, such as observing the rate at which the electrical charge leaked off when hydrogen gas was substituted for air. That the leakage was due to the gas inside the chamber he proved by exhausting the gas or air from the jar and noting that X-rays then had no measurable effect upon the loss of electrical charge from the central wire.

The "electrified air" that Roentgen studied was a major mystery which could not be fully explained until the nature of the atom was better understood. Today we know that ordinarily atoms are electrically neutral—that is, they contain an equal number of negatively and positively charged particles. When an X-ray collides with an atom of air or gas it knocks out a negative particle. It follows, then, that when a unit of negative electricity, called an electron, is jarred out of a neutral atom, the electrical balance is upset and there is left over a positively charged atom. This we call an ion. Ions, in short, are nothing but atoms that have been stripped of an electron by the impact of an X-ray. The process is known as ionization. Unfortunately, Roentgen had no knowledge of the atom's internal structure, so he continued to be puzzled by the electrical effect that X-rays produced in gases.

Since the ions produced in a gas by the passage of X-rays constitute an electrical charge, we can measure this electricity and thus measure the amount of ionization produced by the X-rays. The method is speedy and direct and does away with the slow, tedious process of using photographic film to record X-rays. To make a measuring instrument, it was necessary only to couple a chamber such as we have described (called an ionization chamber) with an electrical measuring device. Such instruments are usually called electroscopes or electrometers. They are nothing more nor less than highly sensitive electrical meters which detect and measure the presence of electrical charges.

A big question still remained unanswered even after Roentgen had done many other X-ray experiments. He had learned,

through one of these experiments, that the X-rays were produced by the impact of the cathode rays (electrons) upon the
metal electrode sealed into the end of the tube. The cathode
rays were stopped in the electrode and in their place the X-rays
were created. One might say that the X-ray was the "death
cry" of the cathode ray. But what was the nature of the X-ray?
Many scientists were inclined to think that it was related to
the ultraviolet ray, but no one could fathom what it really was.

This process, whereby a speeding electron is stopped and
an energetic X-ray is born, is now understood on a theoretical
basis; the details of the theory, however, involve advanced
concepts that need not be introduced here. Suffice it to say
that the laws of physics require that a fast-moving electron
must give up its energy when it slams to a quick halt inside a
metal target, and this energy appears in the form of a packet
of energy (or a quantum or photon) that we call an X-ray.
The faster the electron is hurled (the higher the voltage
across the X-ray tube), the more energetic it is, and the more
energetic and penetrating is the X-ray produced by the electron's impact.

In 1901 the first Nobel Prize in physics was awarded to
Roentgen to honor his great discovery. During his lifetime he
received many more honors, but he shunned publicity. He
loved to roam through Alpine country and climb rugged
mountains. Shortly before his death at the age of seventy-
eight, Roentgen said: "I still prefer to leave the well-worn
path and clamber over bramble and stone. If I should ever be
missing, do not search for me on the main road."

Roentgen could never have imagined the full impact of
his discovery, made on the night of November 8, 1895, when
he traveled off the beaten path. Lesser men might have over-
looked the significance of the fluorescence of the crystals
flashing in the dark. But Roentgen seized upon this single
effect, followed it up with careful experiments and gave the

world something quite new. As we shall see, his discovery sparked the research that led to a series of brilliant discoveries by scientists in other lands. Roentgen's discovery of X-rays marked the end of an era and the beginning of exciting new times in scientific research.

3⃞

Radioactivity

THE celebrated French mathematician and physicist, Henri Poincaré, gave the first details of Roentgen's astonishing discovery to the French Academy of Sciences on January 20, 1896. Poincaré made the assumption that there was a connection between X-rays and the greenish fluorescence that many people had observed at the glass wall of a discharge tube. Roentgen later showed that there was no connection, but at the time the brilliant French scientist thought that the two phenomena went hand in hand.

It was natural that Poincaré should have suggested to his friend, Henri Becquerel, that he investigate whether X-rays were produced by certain substances, mineral salts, which fluoresced under the action of sunlight. Poincaré knew that Becquerel's father had done research on the phosphorescence, the afterglow, of certain crystals exposed to sunlight, and that Becquerel's laboratory held hundreds and thousands of crystal specimens. The possibility that phosphorescence might give rise to X-rays excited Becquerel's imagination and he set to work to find out if it could be true.

Wrapping a small photographic plate in black paper, he placed a crystal of a uranium salt on the package and exposed this to the bright sunlight of a winter's day in Paris. After an exposure of four hours, the French scientist took the package indoors, went into his darkroom and proceeded to develop the photographic plate. Much to his delight, he found that there was a dark smudge on the otherwise clear plate. This blackening corresponded to the outline of the uranium crystal, so Becquerel concluded that the fluorescence that the sunlight had produced in the uranium salt had excited penetrating rays similar to Roentgen's X-rays. Poincaré's hypothesis had apparently been confirmed! On February 24, 1896, Becquerel announced his discovery.

He quickly established that the rays given off by the uranium were penetrating by placing thin sheets of metal between the photographic plate and the crystal. Convinced that it was the sunlight that caused the uranium to emit the penetrating rays, he scanned the skies each morning, hoping for good, sunny weather. But the skies clouded over and only occasionally did a pale sun shine on Paris. Becquerel, disgruntled with the weather, took his packets of plates along with the uranium crystals fixed to them and placed them in a table drawer. Several more days passed with no improvement in the weather and finally, on March 1, 1896, Becquerel decided to develop the plates anyway. Perhaps, he felt, enough sunlight had peeked through the clouds to produce a faint smudge. "On the contrary," Becquerel later observed, "the silhouettes appeared with great intensity." Astonished to find such dense outlines of his uranium sulphate crystals, he quickly verified the fact that certain uranium minerals emitted penetrating rays with no exposure to sunlight. In other words, the emission of the rays was spontaneous and had nothing to do with the phenomenon of fluorescence.

Becquerel repeated his experiment, interposing a sheet of aluminum between the uranium crystal and the photographic plate. He found that the "uranic rays" spontaneously thrown off from the crystal penetrated the aluminum and blackened the photographic plate. All of this happened in complete darkness, so the uranium obviously had the most unusual property of emitting the radiation constantly.

On March 2, 1896, less than two months after the announcement of the discovery of X-rays, Becquerel communicated his results to the French Academy of Sciences. His colleagues were shocked by his discovery. It violated their basic concepts of the unchanging nature of the elements that make up the world and the universe. Yet they respected Becquerel's scientific ability and knew that his results must be true. Becquerel, himself, was convinced that his "uranic rays," as he called them, were identical with Roentgen's X-rays. He found, for example, that the uranium radiation produced ionization in air just as X-rays did. Becquerel was sorely troubled about the real nature of these rays. Moreover, he was quite in the dark about the process by which a uranium atom emitted such radiation.

The element uranium had been discovered in the year 1789. If the discoverer, Martin Klaproth, had used an electroscope to measure his new element he would undoubtedly have found that it caused the instrument to discharge. One can only speculate on what he might have done then. Would he have followed up his finding? Or would he have dismissed it as unimportant? The time was not ripe for such a discovery, a century before Becquerel, and as Lord Rutherford has philosophized: "It is characteristic of science that discoveries are rarely made except when peoples' minds are ready for them."

The scientific world reeled under the twin impact of the discoveries by Roentgen and Becquerel; men were indeed ready for new things. In England, Ernest Rutherford, a young man from New Zealand, arrived at the Cavendish Laboratory and proceeded to study the effect that X-rays had in ionizing gases. He was stimulated by Becquerel's work and he wanted to find out if the ions produced by Roentgen's X-rays and Becquerel's uranic rays were the same. Rutherford's researches were to blaze a trail in the new field of atomic science. We shall devote a later chapter to his investigations.

In France, Becquerel interested a talented professor at the School of Physics and Chemistry in the study of uranium. The young physicist was Pierre Curie, who had married a young Polish girl by the name of Marie Sklodowska. The Warsaw-born girl had studied chemistry at the famous Sorbonne Institute in Paris and it was there that she met Pierre Curie. The two formed a well-matched team, each contributing a different talent to their research.

The Curies set out to discover if uranium was unique in giving off penetrating rays. They devised a sensitive electrometer for measuring the conductivity of air, and with this they studied a variety of substances. They soon discovered that the heavy element thorium also emitted penetrating rays. Thus Becquerel's "uranic rays" were not unique to uranium. In 1898 Marie Curie proposed that the word "radioactivity" be used to describe the emission of radiation from such elements as uranium and thorium.

Stimulated by the fact that thorium was radioactive, the Curies plunged into ceaseless research to investigate the radioactivity of still other substances. In testing mineral after mineral they became intrigued with pitchblende. This mineral was used as a principal source of uranium, which was chemically separated from it by tedious processes. The Curies examined some of the residual material remaining after uranium had been extracted. To their great surprise and bewilderment, they found that the useless pitchblende residue was roughly four times as radioactive as the same amount of uranium. They concluded that this strong radioactivity must be caused by the presence of some unknown substance in the residues from the processing of uranium.

What could this unknown substance be? This was the tantalizing question that triggered a lengthy series of experiments. It was also the question that caused Pierre Curie to give up his research in the electrical properties of crystals and devote full time to working with his wife.

The Curies needed lots of pitchblende, but fortunately they did not require the material as mined; they were anxious to obtain the uranium residues. So they arranged to secure the waste material from the uranium mines at Joachimsthal in Bohemia. These mines had been worked since the fifteenth century for their silver content. Four centuries later they were mined for their pitchblende, the uranium from which was used as a coloring agent in porcelain and glass. The Curies had to work out chemical techniques for processing what amounted to industrial amounts of chemicals. Yet they had little money for their research, very crude laboratory facilities and no staff to help them. They were hunting for an unknown element whose chemistry they could not hope to know in advance; it was like hunting for a needle in a haystack, but much more tedious since they had to handle large vats of noxious acids and chemicals. Their workshop was a crude shack on the outskirts of Paris. On fair days, they worked out of doors, grateful that the weather allowed them to be free of the irritating fumes that bothered them so much on days when they had to work indoors.

Through their arduous chemical work the Curies managed to separate from the uranium residues "a substance whose activity is about 400 times as great as that of uranium. . . . We believe, therefore, that the substance we have isolated from pitchblende contains a hitherto unknown metal." They named the metal polonium after Madame Curie's native country.

Polonium proved to be an important new element, but it was not the complete solution to the mystery that they pursued. They continued their research and in 1898, the day after Christmas, they were able to announce another brilliant discovery. They had succeeded in isolating an element almost one thousand times more radioactive than uranium. To this new, highly radioactive element they gave the name "radium," after the Latin name for "ray."

The Curies could not be sure just how radioactive radium was, because the tiny amount that they separated was mixed with a larger amount of the element barium—a nonradioactive substance. Until they could process more pitchblende and isolate a purer sample of radium, they could only guess at its radioactivity. With characteristic industry and self-sacrifice, the Curies undertook this new task. They managed to obtain a ton of uranium residues from the Joachimsthal mines. Then they began to separate radium from the residues in a long and tedious operation. Pierre Curie took a small sample of radium and deliberately exposed a portion of his arm to the rays. The skin reddened, ulcerated and took over a month to heal from the radium-inflicted wound. Knowing now that the radium was a dangerous substance to work with, they nevertheless continued to work with it day after day. Madame Curie's hands began to show deleterious effects of the radiation; her fingers became numbed, but she worked on. Finally, in 1902, Madame Curie was able to isolate a very significant amount of radium. The activity of pure radium turned out to be a million times greater than that of uranium.

The specimen that was purified in 1902 weighed less than one-hundredth of an ounce. Radium was destined to be both an expensive and a scarce element. Fifty years later the world's supply of the rare element would be reckoned as only five pounds.

Madame Curie completed her work for her doctorate degree in 1904 and in the same year she shared a Nobel Prize with her husband and Henri Becquerel. She refused to take out a patent on the production of radium, maintaining that radium belonged to the people; perhaps she had some foreknowledge of the great medical benefits that her discovery would bring to mankind and wished them to be freely available. Her husband met an untimely death in the spring of 1906, when he was killed in a street accident. Madame Curie, saddened by her loss, devoted herself to research and to bringing up her daughter, who was also to become a famous scientist. Both mother and daughter were to share the same fate—death from the injury caused by constant exposure to radiation. The threat of radiation damage was always with them; Madame Curie herself relates that when she worked at night the bottles and chemical retorts in her laboratory would glow in the dark.

A chance discovery in Germany had triggered the research of Becquerel in France, and this in turn had led to the work of the Curies. But the discoveries left more unexplained than they revealed. The true nature of the rays, the character of radioactivity and the relation of uranium, thorium and radium were still a mystery. It was a scientist in England who found the clues that were to unravel the complicated skein of discoveries. More than any other man, Ernest Rutherford was the master detective who provided the solutions to these complex mysteries.

4

Rutherford: The Great Explorer

ERNEST Rutherford had been greatly excited by Roentgen's discovery of X-rays and he read the subsequent French scientific papers on uranium radiation with much interest. X-rays and radioactivity proved to be the twin discoveries that played a critical role in Rutherford's meteoric career. In the year 1896 Rutherford was a young man of twenty-five, just beginning independent research at the Cavendish Laboratory in England. His early scientific work was guided by Sir. J. J. Thomson, who achieved fame for his investigations of cathode rays, or electrons.

Rutherford had come to the right place to do his research and he had arrived at the right time. Old concepts of matter were being smashed as more and more experimental results gave scientists new insights into the structure of the physical world. Just before the turn of the present century the old, solid world of physicists was crumbling under the impact of radically new ideas. Radioactivity presented scientists with one of their greatest challenges, since it meant that the smallest of all things—the atoms—must themselves be capable of undergoing change. But how these changes took place, how atoms emitted radiation, what this radiation really was—these things were unknown. The brilliant experimentalist, Rutherford, arrived on the scene at this historical time of change to become the great explorer of the unknown.

It should be mentioned that, unlike Roentgen, Rutherford was a team worker. He delighted in sharing his ideas with fellow scientists and in suggesting new experiments to them. Thus the British physicist became the leader of a whole group of co-workers who were drawn to the Cavendish Laboratory and to other places where Rutherford worked.

One of the first problems to interest young Rutherford was the nature of Roentgen's X-rays and Bequerel's "uranic rays." He was also much intrigued by Lenard's experiments with cathode rays. Lenard's success in showing that this fast-moving beam of electrons could penetrate the tissue-thin aluminum window of a discharge tube and emerge on the other side must mean, he thought, that the tiny electrons were slipping through the spaces between the aluminum atoms.

As an experimental physicist, Rutherford devoted himself to planning careful experiments and to devising ingenious apparatus. He put great emphasis upon developing sensitive electrical instruments. His early experiments with the rays given off by uranium were done with an electrometer that measured their ionizing and penetrating power. Bringing a bit of uranium up to the open end of an ionization chamber, he would note the amount of electrical current the rays generated. This was a measure of the total number of ions created in the chamber by the radioactivity. In this way he was able to show that there were two different kinds of rays, for when he slipped a piece of paper between the open end of the chamber and the uranium, the electrical current dropped so sharply it was obvious that only a relatively few rays were getting through. The great majority, which had produced most of the ionization, were being absorbed by the paper. These weaker, "soft" rays Rutherford called "alpha" rays. The others, which had been strong enough to penetrate the paper, he called "beta" rays. These, in general, are stopped by a few sheets of aluminum.

Shortly afterward, the Frenchman Paul Villard discovered a third type of ray given off by uranium that was even more penetrating than the beta ray that Rutherford had found. We call these most penetrating rays "gamma" rays; it may require a thick sheet of lead to absorb them. Gamma rays have precisely the same properties as the X-rays produced by Roentgen with his glass discharge tube.

Puzzled by the fact that a piece of paper could stop the alpha ray, Rutherford began a series of experiments with these rays that were to solve many of the secrets of radioactivity. First, he wanted to find out just what these rays were and to determine their electrical properties. He discovered that they could be bent by a magnet, although not so easily as beta rays. He also measured their weight. What he learned through his various experiments was that the alpha ray consisted of a positively charged bit of matter that was several thousand times heavier than an electron. Actually, it seemed at first that it weighed about twice as much as an atom of hydrogen; later it was shown to weigh four times as much. In short, it turned out that the alpha ray was a fast-moving, rather massive, atomic bullet.

It occurred to Rutherford and to others that if one could measure the total electrical charge given off by a radioactive material, and if one could "count" the number of alpha particles it emitted, then one would know the amount of electrical charge carried per atomic bullet, i.e., per alpha particle. (We shall use the term "ray" or "particle" interchangeably, although alpha ray corresponds to early usage and alpha particle is the more modern term.) To do this experiment, Rutherford had to devise some electrical instrument which would respond to or "count" the passage of a single alpha particle. He teamed up with a young German assistant, Hans Geiger, the mention of whose name introduces the Geiger counter, a most powerful experimental tool for detecting atomic particles. The Geiger counter can be described as a kind of trigger device so sensitive that the passage of a single ionizing particle produces sufficient electricity to initiate a minute spark or avalanche of ions within the gas of the counter tube. Rutherford and Geiger developed a counter tube such that an alpha particle passing into it (through an open window in the end of the tube) produced pulses of electricity which registered as "kicks" on an electrometer. They arranged to photograph these electrometer kicks on a moving photographic film, so that they had a continuous record of the alpha particles entering their counter. At the same time they also measured the total amount of electrical charge produced by their alpha-emitting substance, and in this way they discovered that the electrical charge carried by each alpha particle was equal to that carried by two electrons.

The electron is the smallest unit of electrical charge and is designated by the letter "e". It is negative in sign, so we write "$-e$" for the charge of an electron. In the case of the alpha particle it was shown that the charge was positive, so we write "$+2e$" for the electrical charge of the alpha particle. We shall see in another chapter how this fact fits in nicely with the structure of the atom.

Rutherford was rather firmly convinced by this experiment as well as others that the alpha particle must be an ionized atom of helium. He knew that helium was four times heavier than the hydrogen atom (a fact that fitted in well with his rough measurement of the alpha particle); and furthermore that a helium atom stripped of its electrons would have an electrical charge of $+2e$. But again he wanted positive proof; he wanted to be sure. He reasoned as follows: when the alpha particle stops, it has spent its energy and must join company with two electrons to become a neutral atom of helium. As

long as the alpha particle is moving at high speed, it remains
an ion—that is, it remains electrically charged. It is the fact
that the particle is electrically charged and zips through air
at such high speed that permits it to ionize the atoms of
oxygen (or other gas) through which it passes. A rolling stone
gathers no moss, and a fast-moving alpha particle gathers no
electrons.

In other words, the alpha particle causes electrons to be
ripped away from their parent atoms; it is at this time going
too fast to attract the electrons it jolts loose, as at a slower
speed it might. Thus it converts the gas atoms through which
it travels into gas ions. But with each such collision, the swiftly
moving alpha particle loses some of its energy and slows down.
When it has lost almost all its energy, it can no longer hit
the gas atoms hard enough to knock out electrons, and thus
it loses its ionizing power. Whereupon, Rutherford reasoned,
wouldn't this spent alpha particle, with its positive charge,
pick up two negatively charged electrons and become a normal
atom of helium gas? To test this theory, why not seal up a bit
of radium inside a glass tube so tissue-thin that even weak
alpha particles could manage to penetrate it? Then, if a thicker
glass jacket was put around the inner tube, the spent alpha
particles or helium ions—if that is what they were—converted
to normal atoms of helium gas, should be trapped in the previously evacuated outer chamber. To be sure, the amount of
helium gas that would be collected this way would be small,
but perhaps there would be enough to identify.

The experiment seemed reasonable, so Rutherford went
ahead with it. To identify any traces of helium, he decided to
use a very sensitive technique. He sealed into the outer glass
jacket two small metal electrodes. Then he left the apparatus
alone for a few days to allow time for countless alpha particles
to escape from the inner glass prison into the outer chamber.
Then he and a colleague applied sufficient voltage to the electrodes to cause a low-pressure electrical discharge in the gas,

not enough to produce X-rays but enough to produce a colored streamer of ionized gas in the chamber. When they examined this light with a glass prism spectroscope, the bright lines characteristic of the helium spectrum appeared, proving beyond all doubt that helium had been produced in the experiment. This also provided incontestable proof that alpha particles were indeed atoms of helium stripped of two electrons. We shall see later that atoms of every element have a distinctive spectrum which permits them to be identified. In fact, it was in this way that the element helium was first identified in the sun's spectrum.

Rutherford was also interested in the relation of one element to another in the radioactive series that begins with uranium and ends with lead, and with another co-worker undertook some investigations that eventually enabled them to explain why uranium contains so little radium. To understand this, we have to look into the time it takes for an atom of uranium to transform itself into an atom of lead.

First, we must focus our attention upon how a substance such as radium decomposes in emitting an alpha particle. Suppose we could isolate a single atom or radium and watch it disintegrate. How long would we have to wait for the event? The answer to this question is that nobody knows. The atom might decide to disintegrate immediately, or it might wait for a million years. It is only when we have a crowd—and a very large crowd—of radium atoms that we can study their average behavior. Then if we "count" those that emit alpha particles we do find that radium has a kind of built-in time clock. It is, in fact, an extremely precise device. Accurate measurements show that it takes sixteen hundred years for radium to lose half its radioactivity. Suppose we start today with a small sample of pure radium that emits one million alpha particles each second. About sixteen hundred years from now (around the year 3560), we would find, if we were here to measure it, only half as much activity, or one-half million disintegrations per second. We call this time that it takes for a substance to lose half its activity a half-life. Radioactive material is always dying, but is never quite dead.

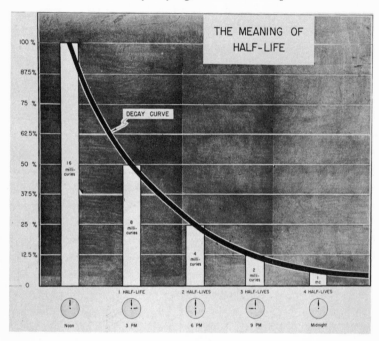

2. A curve illustrating how a radioactive substance decays with the passage of time. If the radioactive material has a half-life of three hours, the decay will be as shown. A curie is the name given to the radioactivity of one gram of pure radium. (Courtesy Atomic Energy Commission)

This strange behavior of a radioactive substance in "losing" its activity is a universal characteristic of all radioactive material. Each has its own unique half-life. Radium, with its half-life of sixteen hundred years, is said to be long-lived; polonium, on the other hand, has a half-life of three minutes, so we call it short-lived. Uranium has an astonishingly long half-life of 4.5 billion years. How can we explain the presence of radium on earth today? Had there been a great amount of it when the planet was formed, one would expect that the passage of almost five billion years would have reduced it to the vanishing point. Yet there must be some explanation to account for its occurrence today.

The clue to this problem is the fact that radium is always found in uranium-bearing minerals. Rutherford cracked the whole problem wide open when he studied the radioactivity of uranium and other radioactive substances. Reduced to its simplest terms, Rutherford analyzed the problem from the viewpoint of what happens to an atom when it emits a charged electrical particle such as an alpha particle. Since an alpha particle is an ion of the element helium, Rutherford argued that the atom which lost such a chunk of matter ought to transform itself into a new element. Certainly, the parent atom must lose weight and electrical charge. To understand the meaning of such a loss of mass and charge, we must pause briefly to look at what we call the Periodic Arrangement of the Elements. We must also consider the weights of atoms.

There are ninety-two elements which occur in nature. These range from a light gas, hydrogen, to a heavy metal, uranium. In between these extremes we find the common gas oxygen, the nitrogen which is so abundant in air, carbon which makes up the bulk of coal, silver, gold and such rare elements as samarium, europium and others which are less well known. The Russian chemist Dmitri Mendeleev, working with the sixty elements known a century ago, found that there were chemical similarities between certain elements. He systematically classified the elements so that those with similar chemical properties were arranged periodically in a table. A modern version of such a Periodic Table of Elements appears on the adjoining page. Note that elements such as lithium (Li), sodium (Na), potassium (K) and cesium (Cs) fall in the same column and all have chemical properties which are similar.

The elements are arranged in this table in order of increas-

	I	II	III	IV	V	VI	VII	VIII	O
1	1 H 1.0078								2 He 4.003
2	3 Li 6.940	4 Be 9.02	5 B 10.82	6 C 12.00	7 N 14.008	8 O 16.0000	9 F 19.00		10 Ne 20.183
3	11 Na 22.994	12 Mg 24.32	13 Al 26.97	14 Si 28.06	15 P 30.98	16 S 32.06	17 Cl 35.457		18 A 39.944
4	19 K 39.096	20 Ca 40.08	21 Sc 45.10	22 Ti 47.90	23 V 50.95	24 Cr 52.01	25 Mn 54.93	26 Fe 55.85 27 Co 58.94 28 Ni 58.69	
	29 Cu 63.57	30 Zn 65.38	31 Ga 69.72	32 Ge 72.60	33 As 74.91	34 Se 78.96	35 Br 79.916		36 Kr 83.7
5	37 Rb 85.48	38 Sr 87.63	39 Y 88.92	40 Zr 91.22	41 Nb 92.91	42 Mo 95.95	43 Tc	44 Ru 101.7 45 Rh 102.91 46 Pd 106.7	
	47 Ag 107.880	48 Cd 112.41	49 In 114.76	50 Sn 118.70	51 Sb 121.76	52 Te 127.61	53 I 126.92		54 Xe 131.3
6	55 Cs 132.91	56 Ba 137.36	57 La 138.92 [*]	72 Hf 178.6	73 Ta 180.88	74 W 183.92	75 Re 186.31	76 Os 190.2 77 Ir 193.1 78 Pt 195.23	
	79 Au 197.2	80 Hg 200.61	81 Tl 204.39	82 Pb 207.21	83 Bi 209.00	84 Po 210	85 At 212.7		86 Rn 222
7	87 Fr 223.7	88 Ra 226.05	89 Ac 227.05	90 Th 232.12	91 Pa 231.7	92 U 238.07			

| RARE EARTHS | 58 Ce 140.13 | 59 Pr 140.92 | 60 Nd 144.27 | 61 Pm 146.0 | 62 Sm 150.43 | 63 Eu 152.0 | 64 Gd 156.9 | 65 Tb 159.2 | 66 Dy 162.46 | 67 Ho 164.94 | 68 Er 167.20 | 69 Tm 169.4 | 70 Yb 173.04 | 71 Lu 174.99 |

3. Periodic arrangement of the elements. Note: Vertical columns (Roman numerals) contain elements with similar chemical properties. Horizontal rows (indicated by Arabic numbers) correspond to successive shells of electrons.

ing atomic weight. Quite arbitrarily, the weight of an atom of oxygen is taken as exactly equal to 16.00000 and all other atoms are compared with the weight of the oxygen atom. On this scale hydrogen has an atomic weight of 1.008, carbon 12.01, iron 55.85, silver 107.880, lead 207.21 and uranium 238.07. Thus an atom of carbon is twelve times heavier than an atom of hydrogen.

In Mendeleev's day the heavy elements beyond lead were mostly "among the missing." As a consequence of the work of Madame Curie and others, it became clear that the newly discovered elements, such as radium, polonium and radon, fitted into place somewhere in the Periodic Table. It was not easy to make determinations of atomic weight, nor was it easy to measure the atomic number of these new elements. The atomic number has much greater significance than merely denoting the relative position which each element occupies in the Periodic Chart. Hydrogen, with atomic number 1, occupies the first space in the table and uranium, with atomic number 92, fills the last space. The atomic number corresponds to the number of positive electrical charges inside an atom—a concept that will be dealt with in the next chapter.

Rutherford perceived that the emission of a charged particle from a heavy atom must change that atom into a different atom—into an atom of another element. In other words, he saw clearly that radioactivity was an explosive process, expelling a particle and leaving a residual atom. The latter, according to Rutherford, must be directly related to the original atom as, so to speak, daughter to parent. We know that an alpha particle has a unit weight of 4 and a positive electrical charge of 2. Therefore, if uranium emits an alpha particle it must disintegrate into a daughter atom weighing 4 units less and having an atomic number 2 units less than that of uranium. Since the atomic number of uranium is 92, this means that the daughter atom must have atomic number 90. Glancing at the Periodic Table, we see that 90 corresponds to the element thorium. Thus Rutherford postulated a kind of modern alchemy—the changing of one element into another.

Experiment showed that his prediction was true. Uranium transforms itself into thorium atoms. This element is also radioactive and in its turn emits an alpha particle. To Rutherford, this could only mean that the uranium-thorium transformation was but the beginning of a chain or series of disintegrations. Radium itself proved to be another link in this chain. Now the various radioelements found their place in the Periodic Table.

Remembering that each radioactive element has atoms with a unique disintegration rate, we may now inquire about the relationship between radium and uranium. Careful measurement of the amount of radium found in undisturbed deposits of pitchblende show that there is only one atom of radium for every 2,800,000 atoms of uranium. The reason that there is so little radium is that somewhere in the series of links from uranium to radium there is a very long-lived parent. It turns out that this is uranium itself.

We may liken the radioactive relationship between uranium and radium to a series of buckets placed on consecutive steps of a stairs. Each bucket has an orifice whose opening may be compared to its half-life; long half-lives correspond to very tiny openings. Water placed in the topmost bucket, corresponding to uranium, trickles out to the next bucket, thorium, which empties quickly (short half-life of about one month) into the next bucket and so on. The amount of liquid reaching the bucket corresponding to radium is determined by the flow rate from the smallest opening; in the uranium-radium series this is the uranium or topmost bucket. Naturally, one has to wait for some time after filling the topmost bucket before what physicists call "equilibrium" sets in. In nature this condition is fulfilled when one uses pitchblende from undisturbed geological deposits.

The chain sequence that we have assumed for the disintegration of radioactive atoms can be verified by using a simple technique. We can make use of specially sensitive photographic plates to record the passage of an alpha particle. As the particle shoots through the photographic emulsion it affects the tiny sensitive crystals, and when the plate is developed we can see the myriad black dots which string together to reveal the track of the particle in much the same way as dirty footprints are left on a clean floor. The accompanying illustration shows a radioactive atom "caught in the act" of emitting alpha particles, which we can see emanating from the specks of polonium embedded in the gelatin of the photographic emulsion. Each stubby black track corresponds to a fast alpha particle emitted in the radioactive series of disintegrations. We call such a picture a "star." Since the distance an alpha particle can travel in the emulsion is only a few thousandths of an inch, we have to magnify the photographic emulsion many times in order to get a photograph such as is shown here.

The other illustration shows what a photoemulsion looks like when clusters of radioactive atoms are exposed for a long time. Then we see clumps of porcupine-like tracks. Each track in the four-pronged cluster represents an alpha particle emitted by, first, the original parent, next the daughter atom, then the granddaughter and finally the great-granddaughter atom. Note that there is a twisting, tortuous track much less dense than the alpha tracks, and that it is much greater in length. This is beta ray (electron), emitted in the radioactive series. (The photograph is made possible by piecing together many separate photos taken at various depths in the emulsion).

Unfortunately, these highly sensitive emulsions were not

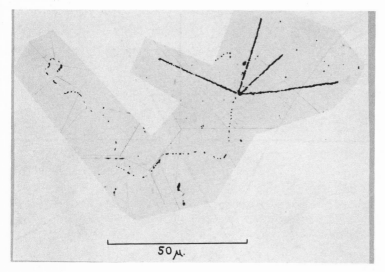

4. A photomicrograph of a "star." The scale of 50 microns (0.002 inch) illustrates the magnification. The four heavy prongs to the star correspond to alpha particles emitted by radioactive thorium byproducts. The meandering thin track is that of a beta particle. (R. H. Herz, Kodak Ltd.)

available in Rutherford's day. He and his colleagues had to unsnarl many of the complications of radioactivity and atomic structure by drawing conclusions from less graphic experimental data. They were quite literally groping in the dark. Moreover, there were many false clues, and the entire terrain of research was so unfamiliar as to confuse even the most alert wayfarer. Rutherford, the giant of his times, surveyed this new territory and claimed it for his own.

5. Photomicrograph of an emulsion impregnated with specks of polonium. Straight tracks corresponding to alpha particles emerge in all directions but only those in the plane of the microscope register in full length. (H. Yagoda, National Institutes of Health, Bethesda, Maryland)

5

The Heart of the Atom

THE concept of the atom originated with the ancient Greeks some five centuries before Christ. The Greeks speculated about the ultimate structure of the world and wondered what would be found if a grain of sand or a drop of water were split into smaller and smaller bits. They supposed that there would eventually be reached a point when the smallest bit of matter could not be cleaved into two parts, and they coined the word "atom," meaning "that which cannot be cut." Unfortunately, they had no tools for carrying out any experiment to put this theory to the acid test; they were content to speculate upon the nature of things.

At the turn of the present century scientists still speculated, but they did more—they turned to the laboratory to put their speculations to the test. They, too, believed in atoms as the smallest entities, too small to be split. Until the discovery of radioactivity, many scientists had been content to view the atom as an infinitesimal billiard ball or as a kind of hard, impenetrable sphere.

It was the electrical nature of the atom that confounded the scientists. Early experiments with electrons perplexed men who could not reconcile the concept of tiny bits of electrical charge in the atom with the solidity of the billiard-ball atom. The advent of radioactivity shook the very foundations of previous concepts of the solidity of the atom, and Rutherford's researches on radioactivity literally "disintegrated the atom." So scientists gave up the idea of the atom as a hard sphere of incredibly small dimensions. The fact that atoms transformed into other atoms in radioactive processes killed the notion that atoms were indestructible. While the emission of an alpha particle from a heavy atom was not exactly a splitting-in-two process, it did involve a splintering of the atom, and this was very convincing to the physicists.

Even before the brilliant experiments of Rutherford illuminated the interior of the atom, men were deeply puzzled by the role that electrons played in the atom's structure. Lenard, in observing how easily the electrons of his cathode rays pierced an aluminum foil, speculated that the atom was far from solid and must be rather empty inside. It appears that J. J. Thomson was the first to perceive that electrons must exist as separate and dominating entities within the atom. In the same year that radium was discovered he stated: "I regard the atom as containing a larger number of corpuscles [electrons]," and he described the atom as an electrically neutral system in which there were positive charges that balanced out the negative electrons. Thomson seems to have had a picture of the atom as a sphere of positive electricity punctuated by electrons. Later he enlarged upon this picture by assuming that the electrons arranged themselves in concentric shells. With a flash of genius, he saw a relation between the shell-like layers of electrons and the chemical and physical properties of the elements. In other words, he identified the electron shells as determining the chemical properties of the various elements. He had the germ of an idea that would later be developed to provide a neat explanation of the chemical behavior of the elements. This will be discussed in the next chapter.

It is astonishing to look back into the history of these atomic pioneer days and find that a Japanese scientist by the name of Hantaro Nagaoka saw a resemblance between the structure of the atom and that of a heavenly body. His view of the atom was that electrons moved about a central positive charge much as satellites move around a planet. However, little attention was paid to this concept. Men were skeptical about accepting new ideas without experimental data to back them up.

New ideas were popping up in many places as a result of the revolutionary new developments in physics. In 1905, Albert Einstein came forth with a radically different concept, so new that it was hard to believe—his Special Theory of Relativity. Mass and energy were intimately related, Einstein claimed, and he produced a simple equation relating the two quantities. If we let m stand for mass and E represent energy, then the Einstein relation says $E = mc^2$ where c^2 is the square of the velocity of light, an unchanging factor. Einstein also had some other things to say that were equally shocking to long-held concepts of scientists, but we shall focus briefly upon his mass-energy relation.

Mass to most people has a rather substantial meaning; it is weight. Energy is a term that has less tangible significance to most people. There are many kinds or forms of energy—kinetic energy or energy of motion, as for example that which a fast-moving bullet possesses or the energy of a Sputnik circling the earth in endless orbits. We describe physical quantities such as mass and energy in very specific physical units, the nature of which is apt to be rather foreign to non-scientists. Mass, for example, we can measure in grams (453.6 grams equals one pound). The velocity of light is measured in terms of 186,000 miles per second or, to use scientific units, thirty billion centimeters per second (2.54 centimeters equal 1 inch).

Let's see what the consequence of Einstein's $E = mc^2$ is

when we let m equal one pound or 453.6 grams and c equal thirty billion centimeters per second. This should tell us the energy to which one pound of mass is equivalent. Multiplying the values together, we find that E equals 4 followed by 23 zeros. But what does such an astronomic value as 400,000,-000,000,000,000,000,000 mean? In terms of the units that we used, the result of multiplying grams by centimeters per second yields energy as measured in ergs. This may be an unfamiliar unit, so we shall hastily translate it into calories, asking that it be accepted on faith that 1 calorie equals 42 million ergs. So dividing our astronomic number above by 42 million, we get approximately (in round numbers) 10,000,-000,000,000,000 calories.

Chemists tell us that a ton of high explosive like TNT releases one billion calories when it is exploded. Therefore, dividing this number into our figure of ten million billion calories of energy associated with one pound of matter, we see that the pound of matter is equal to ten million tons of TNT! This fantastic result seems absolutely incredible. How in the world can such a small thing as one pound of matter be the equivalent of ten million tons of TNT?

To answer this question, we must go back to Einstein's assumptions. His relation states that this equivalence between mass and energy is real, but it gives no clue to how such energy might be released. It simply says that if *all* the atoms in a pound of matter could be instantly and totally converted into energy, an explosion would take place which would equal that from the detonation of ten million tons of TNT. However, Einstein's relation applies to less drastic situations, as, for example, the burning (chemical combustion) of a lump of coal. In the combustion process carbon unites with oxygen to form carbon dioxide, and energy is released in the form of heat. Solids unite with gas to form a gas. We can calculate, as in our previous example, that in the process of burning a pound of coal some mass is converted (on an

Einsteinian $E = mc^2$ basis) into energy. But the fact of the matter is that $E = mc^2$ had little practical meaning for people half a century ago; it was beyond the world of ordinary experience.

No one knew what the inner structure of the atom was, and although people did speculate about the atom's energy, it was futile talk since this energy was beyond the reach of man. Chemical processes such as the burning of coal were not affected by Einstein's revolutionary new theory. However, men such as Rutherford realized that the atom possessed great energy. They knew, for example, that a gram of radium was self-heating, giving off about one hundred calories of energy every hour. This energy was of atomic origin and resulted from the disintegration process by which alpha particles were emitted and gave up their energy in the form of heat.

An alpha particle emitted by a heavy atom carries off considerable energy. The disintegration process imparts high speed to the relatively massive atomic bullet. Just as an ordinary bullet is propelled out from a gun barrel by the sudden release of energy (expansion of hot gases from gunpowder exploding) so, too, the alpha particle is shot out as the result of some energy change within the atom. This was, indeed, a profound puzzler. Where did the alpha bullet get its enormous energy? This was equivalent to saying, what happened inside the atom? How could anyone answer such a question when no one knew what the inside of an atom was like?

Rutherford approached this problem shortly after Einstein's theory was announced. He and Dr. Geiger had been studying the properties of alpha particles; they noticed that when alpha particles traversed thin foils of heavy metals some of the particles were deflected from their straight-line course and shot off in different directions. This "scattering" of the alpha particles was a small effect and Rutherford thought that since even the thinnest metallic foil was many, many atoms thick, the alpha particle might swerve a little from its course as the result of innumerable encounters with the atoms in the foil. It did not seem very significant, but one day in 1909 Dr. Geiger came to Rutherford and suggested that a man, Ernest Marsden, whom he was training, ought to be given a research problem. "Why not let him see if any alpha particles can be scattered through a large angle?" was the reply Rutherford gave him. Rutherford never thought that anything would come of it but that it would be good experience for the young man.

A few days later Geiger burst in upon Rutherford and in obvious excitement blurted out, "We have been able to get some of the alpha particles coming backward."

The experiment that Geiger and Marsden had performed was a straightforward one. They used a bit of radioactive material as a source of alpha particles, and aligned it in a tube containing metal shields perforated with pinholes that excluded all but those alpha particles traveling in a straight line forward. This beam of alpha particles was then allowed to impinge upon a very thin metallic foil of gold or platinum less than a thousandth of an inch thick. Around this foil they arranged a rotatable little screen of zinc sulphide which would record the arrival of a single alpha particle as a tiny flash of light. They evacuated the tube so that the alpha particles would not be slowed down by the air. Then, putting the little screen in the "line of fire" or straight down the axis of the tube, they counted the alpha particles that whizzed through the foil without appreciable deflection. They moved the screen at an angle to this beam and again counted the tiny flashes of light. Much to their surprise, they were able to record alpha particles, a very few to be sure, zooming off at right angles to the beam! They even found some that were scattered through more than a right angle and headed back toward the source.

"It was the most incredible event that has ever happened to me in my life," Rutherford wrote later. "It was almost as incredible as if you fired a 15 inch shell at a piece of tissue paper and it came back and hit you."

Rutherford pondered over the dramatic encounter that the alpha particle made in colliding with an atom in the metallic foil. He crossed off the possibility that many successive encounters were involved, since this would simply scatter the particle back and forth and not deflect it at such a wide angle. So it had to be a single encounter with an atom. Now Rutherford plunged into the heart of the matter. Did the alpha particle merely skim the surface of the atom, or did it crash deep into the core of the atom? Rutherford was able to show that in order for an alpha particle to be scattered so abruptly off its course it would have to make a "close collision"—that is, it would have to come within a very small distance of a concentrated electrical charge. If the atom's electrical charge were uniformly distributed in a cloudlike sphere, the alpha particle would not be kicked out of its path so sharply. He developed a model for this nuclear atom and calculated that an alpha particle would shoot off at a definite angle if it came within a certain distance of this positively charged nucleus. His calculations and the data from experiments on the scattering of alpha particles checked.

The centuries-old concept of the hard, billiard-ball atom was shattered. Rutherford substituted a new model that pictured the atom as a kind of miniature solar system. Later, in describing the birth of the nuclear theory of the atom, he cited the whole episode as an "example to show how you often stumble upon facts by accident."

By accident or by intent, there was little doubt that Rutherford had penetrated to the very heart of the mystery about the atom's structure. In place of our sun there is the small, positively charged nucleus containing the great mass of the atom. At quite large distances away (in relative terms) electrons arrange themselves like planets around the sun. This was an electrical concept of the atom that made the atom, like our solar system, mostly space dotted here and there with globs of matter. The Japanese physicist Nagaoka had had the right intuition about the atom after all. But it was Rutherford who converted the alpha-particle-scattering experiment into a new theory.

Rutherford's startling theory was published in 1911, after he had convinced himself that the experiments permitted only one conclusion—that the atom must have a tiny, but heavy nucleus containing almost all of the atom's mass. He was even able to demonstrate that the nucleus must be infinitesimally small, occupying only $1/100,000$ as much space as the atom itself.

It is interesting to note that the alpha particles that created so many questions about the atom were used as the means to provide the answers to these very questions. However, they did not resolve all the questions, for still no one could explain the radioactive disintegration process itself. There were huge gaps in basic knowledge, which could not be filled in very quickly. But each experiment added to the sum of knowledge, and each man built upon an inheritance of his predecessor's experience. The alpha-particle-scattering experiment depended upon discoveries by Roentgen, Becquerel, the Curies and many others. Furthermore, their apparatus represented a combination of techniques which were the contributions of many scientists.

Instruments were of the greatest importance since scientists were working with such small, invisible particles. Instruments and techniques were required to make really meaningful experiments possible. The fluorescent screen, the photographic plant and the ion counter all represented highly useful devices for doing atomic research. Just about the time when Rutherford was announcing his theory of the nuclear atom, a British colleague perfected a radically new method of observing happenings in the atomic world. C. T. R. Wilson developed an instrument known as a cloud chamber for visualizing the track of an ionizing particle.

The Wilson cloud chamber works on the principle that if an enclosed gas (air) is expanded, it will cool, and if the gas is saturated with water vapor, the vapor will condense out in the form of droplets. When there is no dust present to form a point for condensation, the water vapor will form upon any ions that may be present. Dr. Wilson made a cylinder topped with a flat glass plate through which he could observe what happened inside. Opposite this plate was a piston which could move back and forth to compress and expand the air inside the cloud chamber. A bright light was focused so that it illuminated the inside of the chamber. Dr. Wilson showed that if a bit of radioactive material was placed at one side of the chamber, and the chamber was expanded properly, a cloud of tiny water droplets would condense out on the trail of ions left by the ionizing particle.

The line tracks left by alpha particles are clearly seen in a photograph. They are characterized not only by a general straightness of path but by an abrupt stoppage or a definite range. If we examine an alpha track closely we can actually count the little droplets and thus count the number of ions created by the alpha particle as it swept through the chamber. One can show for example that most particles produce about 200,000 ions over the length of their path. We can now estimate the energy of a single alpha particle by multiplying this number by the energy required to ionize atoms in air. Experiments show that it takes about 32 electron volts (ev) of energy to convert a neutral atom into an ion. The electron volt is a unit of energy that we shall have occasion to use frequently, so we shall explain it now. An electron in a TV tube may be accelerated by 18,000 volts of electrical power. We say that this electron acquires an energy of 18,000 ev or 18 kev (kilovolts). In the same way we say that an ion hurled along by a two million volt potential has an energy of 2 Mev—the M standing for million. To return an estimate of the energy of the alpha particle, we see that 32 (the energy needed to ionize one atom) multiplied by 200,000 (the num-

6. A Wilson cloud chamber 12 inches in diameter is used at the Brookhaven National Laboratory for atomic research. The technician points to the top of the chamber, through which photographs of droplet tracks are made. (Brookhaven National Laboratory)

ber of ions created by a single alpha particle) gives us 6,400,-000 ev or 6.4 Mev for the energy of a single alpha particle.

Alpha particles emitted by radioactive substances are therefore high-energy atomic projectiles. They are shot out with speeds of about 10,000 miles per second. As they race through a gas they cause it to be ionized, because the double positive charge of the alpha particle attracts the negative electrons in the outer part of the atoms of gas. This attraction is so great that electrons are pulled out of their parent atoms, thus producing ions. As we have pointed out earlier, it takes energy to ionize an atom, so the alpha particle continues to lose energy with each collision it makes as it proceeds on its course.

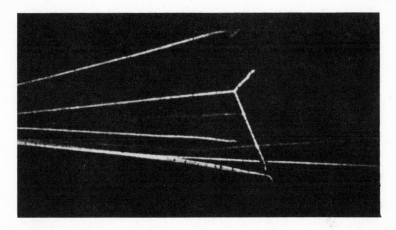

7. Cloud chamber picture of an alpha particle colliding with an atom of oxygen. (P. M. S. Blackett)

Some years after the original experiments on the scattering of alpha particles, the use of the cloud chamber revealed the dramatic nature of a chance encounter between an alpha particle and an atom of oxygen. The oxygen was present as a gas inside the cloud chamber, and because a gas has so many fewer atoms in the same space than a sheet of metal, the scattering of an alpha particle by an atom of gas is a rare event. The accompanying photograph shows one of these rare events which occurs when an alpha particle happens to make a close collision with the heart of an oxygen atom. The alpha particle is shown as the second track from the top, proceeding in its accustomed straight-line path. At the point indicated by the fork in the track the alpha particle is deflected toward the bottom of the picture where it stops. The shorter, stubby track proceeding toward the top of the picture is the oxygen nucleus recoiling away from the collision. It is more massive and hence does not travel so far in the gas. We say that the collision is elastic and we may liken it to a golf ball hitting a billiard ball on a pool table. The golf ball (corresponding to the alpha particle) is smaller and lighter so it bounces off the heavier billiard ball; the latter recoils for a short distance in comparison to the ricochet of the golf ball. One can see that such photographs as the cloud chamber makes possible are of the greatest significance in understanding events that take place on an atomic scale.

Rutherford's model of the atom as a nucleus surrounded by a swarm of circulating electrons assumes that the number of positive charges in the nucleus is equal to the number of negatively charged electrons in the orbits of the atom. Rutherford recognized that it was the orbiting electrons that gave form to the atom. He also realized that an alpha particle smashing into an atom of gold or platinum with a great abundance of such orbital electrons would be far more likely to pass close to these than to the single, small nucleus. Therefore, would it not be probable that these electrons could cause the oncoming alpha particle to deviate from its straight-line path? Rutherford showed that the alpha-particle-electron encounters, while more frequent than nucleus encounters, could not deflect the much more massive (thousands of times heavier) alpha particle. Moreover, the electron has only a single electrical charge whereas a nucleus of gold has 79 positive charges. An elephant can plow through a stand of bamboo without trouble, but when a huge tree blocks his way he has to turn aside.

What of the 79 orbital electrons in the gold atom? What of the 79 positive charges in its nucleus? What were the positive charges? How did the electrons arrange themselves around the nucleus? What kept them in orbit? These were questions that were left unanswered at the time, and while Rutherford was to help answer many of them, it remained for a Danish scientist, Niels Bohr, to unravel the mysterious secrets of the outer part of the atom.

The Bohr Atom

RUTHERFORD breached the ramparts of the atom and revealed that the atom is mostly space, that the nucleus contains the great mass of the atom and that orbital electrons whirl around the nucleus in never-ending spirals. However, Rutherford could not explain the outer structure of the atom—the shells of electrons that surround the nucleus.

A great theoretical physicist from Copenhagen proposed a theory that went far toward explaining the outer atom. Niels Bohr, along with many others in the scientific community, had been puzzled by a wealth of data which tantalized everyone, because it showed that there must be some orderly scheme of things inside the atom. For example, we have already mentioned that helium gas emits definite kinds of light when electricity is passed through it. These sharp lines of light, corresponding to various colors, can be measured with optical intruments to a high degree of accuracy. Helium emits its unique lines of light; hydrogen also has its own family of lines or wave lengths, and so on for every element. The lines arrange themselves on a photographic plate in a spectrum of singular regularity. (See illustration.) The series of lines can even be represented by mathematical relationships, clearly implying some definite kind of order within the atom.

8. Simple optical spectrum of hydrogen. The light is split up by a glass prism. Each spectral line corresponds to a definite electron jump between two orbits in the hydrogen atom.

The characteristic spectral lines emitted by each element become more numerous and complex as one goes from hydrogen to uranium in the Periodic Table. Some concept of the complexity and number of these lines is given in the illustration showing the spectral lines produced in the hot gap of an iron arc (the blazing gas formed between two iron electrodes).

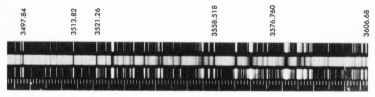

9. A very small part of the ultraviolet spectrum of iron vapor (top and bottom strips) and sun (central strip). The entire spectrum from ultraviolet to infrared contains thousands of lines. Each line represents an electron jump from one orbit to another and corresponds to a definite wave length measured to six significant figures.

The lines sandwiched in the strip between the two spectra of iron correspond to those emitted by the sun. Naturally, the sun contains a great many elements, but one can see from the photograph that the sun emits lines that are identical with those produced in the iron arc. This proves that the sun contains iron. It was in this way that the element helium was first identified as a constituent of the sun even before it was found on earth.

The Bohr theory of the atom's structure sought to and did explain the spectra of hydrogen and other elements. Dr. Bohr

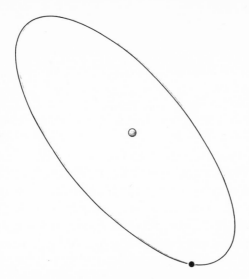

10. Hydrogen-1, the simplest of all atoms, consists of a single proton as its nucleus and a single orbital electron. The size of the nucleus is enlarged with respect to the size of the atom. The atom appears as one billion times its actual size.

assumed that in the case of hydrogen, the atom consisted of a massive central nucleus carrying one positive electrical charge and a single electron which whirled about the nucleus. We see that Bohr adopted the nuclear theory supplied by his good friend Rutherford. In making this assumption Bohr was not proposing anything novel. Others had speculated about an atomic model consisting of a single hydrogen nucleus (which we shall call a proton, although at the time of the Bohr theory this name had not been adopted) and a single orbital electron. The trouble with this model was that since the proton and electron are of opposite electrical charge they should attract each other, and the electron should spiral into the nucleus. This would be catastrophic, not only for an atomic theory but for the whole universe. It obviously does not happen, but why not? Why do the electrons whirl ceaselessly in speedy orbits the same today as in Roman times or in prehistoric times?

It would be tempting to offer an explanation based upon the solar system. Our planet spins around the sun in a giant orbit, with an average distance of 93 million miles from sun to earth. Since it takes one year for the earth to complete an orbit, we know that the earth's average orbital speed is 66,000 miles per hour. But why does the earth continue to circle the sun? The gravitational force between the sun and earth should pull them together. However, the earth is in motion and as a result of its motion there is a strong centrifugal force which would cause it to zoom out like a drop from a rapidly spinning wheel if it were not for the constant gravitational attraction of the sun. The two forces exactly balance each other.

Nowadays this is not hard to believe because we have Sputniks or satellites spinning around our globe. They are carefully shot into orbit at the right speed so that their trajectory forms a stable orbit. Earth satellites have to attain a velocity of six miles per second in order to orbit. If there were no resistance to their motion—i.e., if there were no air or resistive force at work, artificial satellites would stay in orbit forever. But because there is a little "friction," the earth satellites lose energy and spiral into the earth's atmosphere, ending up as an incandescent streak in the sky.

Our own planet glides around the sun in a frictionless void, so it does not suffer the fate of a Sputnik; for the same reason the moon orbits ceaselessly around the earth. Electrons also gyrate around the atomic nucleus in a friction-free space. However, according to the laws of physics, electrons traveling in orbit at the speed they do—a speed hundreds of times greater than a Sputnik's—would have to give off energy in the form of radiation. Losing energy would cause them to drop into lower and lower orbits closer to the nucleus, and finally to dive into the nucleus itself.

Bohr made the rash assumption that the classical picture was wrong; he proposed instead that electrons could move in fixed orbits without radiating energy. To each orbit there is a definite amount of energy ascribed, and when the electron is circulating in this orbit, it stays in a "stationary state" without losing energy. It is only when the atom absorbs energy, as from violent agitation in a gas discharge tube, that the electron jumps from one orbit to another and in the process emits energy in the form of light. Since there are many possible orbits for the electron, there are many possible combinations or jumps that the electron can make. Each jump corresponds to a pulse of light or a different color of radiation given off by the atom. Now we begin to see what the regularity of the lines in an element's spectrum really means. It is the direct result of there being definite electron orbits inside an atom.

In other words, the bold new look which Dr. Bohr gave to the atom's structure was that of an ordered number of orbits in which the electrons might circulate. Radiation—meaning, usually, rays of light of a definite color corresponding to the spectral lines we discussed—is emitted whenever the electrons jump down from one orbit to another. Since Bohr specified that only certain regularly spaced orbits are permissible and that specific energy is associated with each orbit, it was clear that each electron jump would involve a definite amount of energy. This meant that each electron jump from one orbit to another corresponds to one of the spectral lines, such as those shown in the illustration of the hydrogen atom's spectrum. A simple system consisting of a single proton and one orbital electron (the simple hydrogen atom) has only a certain allowed number of orbits and therefore a relatively small number of electron jumps, each of which corresponds to a line in the hydrogen spectrum.

Not all the problems were resolved by Bohr's theory, which he proposed in 1913 while working at the University of Manchester in association with Rutherford. But the groundwork was done for building up a new picture of the atom's structure. Physicists had a model in which they could place some confidence. Obviously the structure of more complex atoms, such as iron with twenty-six orbital electrons, would be more complicated. How, for example, did these electrons arrange themselves around the nucleus?

According to the Bohr model, the outermost electrons were the ones responsible for the optical spectra. Put another way, the outermost electrons were farther from the nuclear charge and were therefore more loosely "bound" to the nucleus. These electrons were thus easier to detach and to move around than the inner electrons. It was these outermost electrons that played such a big role in the chemical properties of atoms. These were also the electrons knocked out most easily by the process of ionization.

Recalling the properties of elements such as sodium and potassium and the others that align themselves in one column of the Periodic Table, we can make the assumption that the reason these elements behave in a similar chemical fashion is that in each one the outermost electron is "free." Let's look

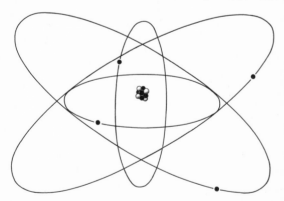

11. A schematic "view" of a light atom (beryllium) showing the compact nucleus (much enlarged) and four orbital electrons.

at the systematic progression of the atomic numbers of these elements. Hydrogen has atomic number 1 and therefore 1 orbital electron; lithium has 3, sodium 11, potassium 19, rubidium 37, cesium 55—all have odd numbers of electrons. If we

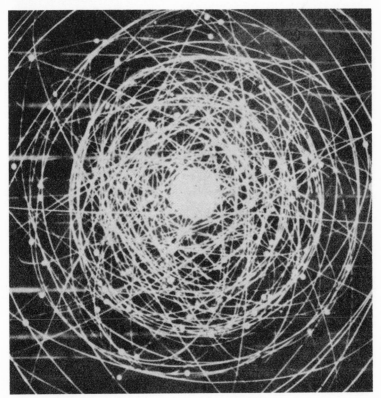

12. A model showing electron orbits in a heavy atom. The size of the nucleus is out of proportion in scale. (Courtesy U.S. Information Service)

subtract each number from the following one we get the following sequence: 2, 8, 8, 18, 18. If we look at the last column in the Periodic Table, starting with helium with atomic number 2, we have neon (10), argon (18), krypton (36) and xenon (54)—all even numbers. Again the same sequence turns

13. A diagrammatic view of a heavy rare earth element (atomic number 71—lutetium), showing the various groups and subgroups of electron shells. These shells are labeled K, L, M, N and so forth, starting with the innermost ring of two electrons.

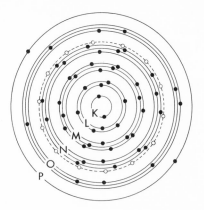

up if we subtract atomic numbers, for we get 8, 8, 18 and 18. The notable thing about the last-mentioned elements is that they are all inert or noble gases which do not combine chemically with other elements. On the other hand, elements such as sodium and potassium have a great affinity for joining chemically with other elements, such as chlorine. Table salt is a stable compound of sodium and chlorine or NaCl.

Since the inert gases refuse to exhibit chemical attraction for other elements, it is tempting to assume that their electrons must form closed shells. In effect, combinations of 2, 8, 18 and so on electrons form exclusive groups. Sodium has two closed shells of 2 and 8 electrons each, and has only one electron in its outermost orbit. Chlorine, on the other hand, has 17 electrons arranged in shells of 2, 8 and 7 electrons. In other words, it lacks but one electron of completing a closed shell. When a chlorine and a sodium atom are brought together they undergo a mating or a union. The lone, outer electron of the sodium atom "fills" the vacancy in the uncompleted last shell of the chlorine atom. Thus we have a sharing of this electron. And as a consequence we have a stable molecule of one atom of sodium and one atom of chlorine—or NaCl, salt.

The model we describe consists then in a regular arrangement of electron shells banked around the nucleus. The first shell is filled with 2 electrons, the next with a total of 8, the next 18 and so on. This regularity in the build-up of the electrons into systematic shells suggests strongly that there is some fundamental structural design to the atom. The explanation of this intricate architecture had to await the development of radically new theories about the nature of the atom—theories that were to revolutionize physics in the 1920s. To describe the building-up principle of the electron shells would take us far afield from our present inquiry into the atom, so let us get back to the researches of scientists during the World War I decade.

Before we do, however, we should recognize that our picture of the atom as mostly space is apt to violate a layman's feeling for the solidness of things. How can the atom be largely "empty space" and yet account for the rigidness of, say, strong metals?

First, remember that the nucleus of a hydrogen atom weighs almost two thousand times more than its single electron. Yet all this mass is concentrated in a tiny, compact nucleus deep within the atom. The electron is a whirling dervish which flashes around this central proton at two hundred times the speed of a Sputnik circling the earth. Next, we may ask how many times per second the electron orbits around the proton. This requires that we know the approximate diameter of the hydrogen atom. We can determine this in a variety of ways; for example, we can liquefy hydrogen gas and then estimate the size of the atom. It turns out that the diameter of the H atom is 1/200,000,000 inch. A little arithmetic shows that the electron makes a billion trips around its orbit in a millionth of a second!

Having these facts in mind, we can begin to see why the atom has substance. The electrons fly around the outer parts of the atom so fast that they are everywhere at once. One way of visualizing this is to assume that in the hydrogen atom the orbital electron emits a thin trail of smoke as it travels. If you rigged up a hypothetical camera which could take a "picture" of the atom and freeze the motion to one-billionth of a second, you would never catch the electron. All you would see would be the spherical smoke screen it left behind. Thus it is the everywhere-at-once nature of the electron in the atom that gives form to it. The cloudlike picture of the atom conforms better to the modern view of atomic structure than the planetary picture of Dr. Bohr's day.

If we shift our attention from the lightest atom to the heaviest, we must visualize a densely packed core weighing 238 times as much as the hydrogen nucleus. Around this small, central core a total of 92 electrons are arranged in orderly shells. But 99.95 per cent of the mass of the atom resides in the tiny nucleus. And since we have seen that mass (or matter) and energy are interrelated by Professor Einstein's rule, we must conclude that the great bulk of the atom's energy is concentrated in the nucleus. It is to the nucleus that we must look for any real source of atomic energy. Almost instinctively, Rutherford concentrated his attack upon the nucleus, leaving the outer structure of the atom for others to explore and explain. Again it was the great British physicist who performed the critical experiment that was to illuminate the nature of the nucleus.

7º

The Atom Is Splintered

In the course of a visit to the United States before the outbreak of World War I, Lord Rutherford had predicted: "It is possible that the nucleus of an atom may be altered by the direct collision of the nucleus with atoms of helium such as are ejected from radioactive matter." In other words, the British dean of nuclear scientists believed not only that alpha particles might be abruptly altered in their course, as in the famous scattering experiment, but that some of them might score a direct hit upon the nucleus.

Rutherford had to wait until after the war to return to his laboratory and put his idea to the proof test of experiment. The apparatus he devised is shown in the illustration. It con-

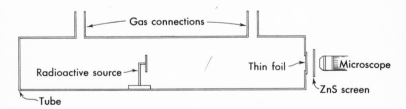

14. Diagram of Rutherford's equipment for observing the first man-made nuclear disintegration.

sisted of a long glass cylinder which could be filled with gas. At one end of this tube Rutherford placed a small source of alpha particles (a decay product of radium) which could be moved back and forth in the tube. He fixed a very thin foil over an opening in the other end of the tube and placed a zinc sulphide screen, as shown. A microscope was adjusted to view the flashes of light given off from the screen when it was struck by charged particles.

When the tube was filled with oxygen Rutherford determined that no scintillations could be observed on the screen when it was more than seven centimeters away from the alpha source. This, then, was the maximum range, i.e., distance of travel, of the alpha particles emitted by the particular radioactive source he was using. Upon removing the oxygen and filling the tube with nitrogen, he observed that flashes of light were given off by the screen even when it was more than seven centimeters distant from the radioactive source. In fact, he moved the screen four times this distance and still observed some light flashes. Obviously, some long-range charged particles were being produced by the impact of the alpha particles on the atoms of nitrogen.

Rutherford checked his experiment carefully and finally summed up his conclusion: "It is difficult to avoid the conclusion that these long-range atoms arising from the collision of alpha particles with nitrogen . . . are probably charged atoms of hydrogen." In other words, he assumed that alpha particles struck the nuclei of nitrogen atoms and ejected protons. Note that Rutherford used the word "probably" in stating his conclusion. He could not be certain that the long-range particles were protons, since all he had was circumstantial evidence. But he reasoned that a proton, having only one-fourth the mass and one-half the charge of an alpha particle, could be expected to travel much farther in the gas; indeed, the proton was about the only particle that Rutherford knew of that could fill the bill.

Not many years later, cloud chamber studies showed that his conclusion was correct—protons were indeed knocked out of nuclei by the rare collision of an alpha particle with a nitrogen nucleus. When we say a rare collision, we can be more specific; only one alpha particle in a million produces a proton. All the rest shoot by the tiny citadel of the nucleus without penetrating its defenses. The reason for the rarity of the event is that the high positive charge on the nitrogen nucleus repels the great majority of the oncoming alpha particles.

It took great patience for P. M. S. Blackett to photograph the rare event studied by Rutherford in 1919. But after taking over 23,000 cloud chamber pictures and examining almost one-half million alpha tracks Dr. Blackett found proof, as shown in the illustration. Alpha particles streak into the cloud chamber from the left, leaving their straight, undeviating tracks. However, the topmost track kinks abruptly and

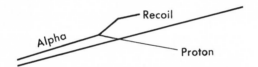

15. Alpha particles are shown passing through nitrogen gas in a cloud chamber. The topmost alpha particle collides with a nitrogen nucleus and ejects a proton. The residual nucleus (oxygen) recoils to the upper right.

thickens where the side spur branches off. Blackett identified the longer, less dense and straight track as belonging to a proton. What then was the stubby track?

We know that nitrogen has atomic number 7 and that its atomic nucleus possesses 7 protons. We also know that the alpha particle has a double positive charge owing to its 2 protons, each of which, of course, has a single positive charge. Scientists assume that in all processes such as we are considering the total electrical charge must be conserved. By that we mean that starting with the two partners in the reaction, namely, nitrogen and the alpha particle, we have a charge of $7 + 2 = 9$. We cannot destroy any of this total charge, although we may divide it up. In our cloud chamber photograph we identify one of the end products of the reaction as a proton. Therefore we deduce that, since the charge is conserved, the identity of the other end product must be a particle with 9 minus 1 or 8 positive charges. This we know from the Periodic Tables is the atomic number of oxygen, so we conclude that the recoil nucleus in this case is oxygen.

Rutherford's bombardment of nitrogen with alpha particles resulted in the first successful smashing of the atomic nucleus. Even though the bulk of the atom had not been split in two, nonetheless it had been splintered. It was the beginning of a new chapter in science, one that could be titled "Nuclear Reactions." By chipping away at the core of the atom scientists were to gain fundamental knowledge about the mystery of mysteries—the forces that held the smaller pieces of the tiny nucleus together.

The sum total of nuclear knowledge when Rutherford chipped off a piece of the nitrogen nucleus was not very impressive. The nucleus was known to be a dense, hard object, but no one knew very much about its constituents. There were protons inside the nucleus, to be sure, but it was thought there must be something else, since a heavy atom like uranium has only 92 protons but weighs almost 238 times more than a proton. Then, too, there was the puzzling question of how the nuclear particles stuck together; what kind of nuclear glue was responsible for this cohesion? The alpha particle, for instance, was known to be four times as heavy as a proton, though in fact it must contain only two protons. It was reasonable to assume that it contained two more constituents about the same weight as a proton but without the proton's electrical charge. To this puzzling neutral particle the name "neutron" was given. Thus, although there was no proof of their existence, neutrons were assumed to be the other constituents of the nucleus. (In fact, they were thought of at first as a kind of neutralized proton, a combination of a proton and a negative electron, so that the electrical charges canceled out.) As we shall see later, it was not until 1932 that the neutron was proved to be a separate nuclear particle without any electrical charge whatever. In the case of the alpha particle, how were the four nuclear constituents, the two neutrons and the two protons, held together? What happened when the alpha particle smashed into a nitrogen nucleus? Was the alpha particle swallowed up by the nucleus and a proton ejected? These were all questions that confounded the early experimenters as they tried to understand Rutherford's experiment.

Just as these men were struggling to think through the meaning of the nucleus, a new field of research blossomed which was to be of immense value in the study of nuclear reactions. This was the field of accurate atom-weighing, which is technically known as mass spectroscopy. Scientists had suspected that not all the atoms of any element were the same weight. They based their case on a variety of clues. For example, over three dozen different radioactive species of atoms had been identified among the heavy elements in the neighborhood of radium and uranium. Yet there were only ten basic elements to which these radioactive species could belong, since no radioactive elements existed below lead (atomic number 82) in the Periodic Table. Furthermore, chemists showed that certain radioactive species had exactly the same chemistry. In addition, when they analyzed lead from different mineral deposits, they found that this stable lead, which is the end of the radioactive series, had an atomic weight of about 206 when found in association with uranium minerals, and roughly 208 when found with minerals containing thorium. This meant that there were atoms of different weight belonging to the same chemical element. Such atoms are known as isotopes.

F. W. Aston in England and A. J. Dempster in the United States designed an atom-weighing machine, called a mass spectrograph, which separated the isotopes of an element so that they could be identified. For our purpose, we need know little more about these machines than that they are devices that twist the charged atoms of an element through magnetic and electric fields and line up the atoms thus separated into beams, according to their weight. The beams show up as individual lines on a photographic plate. By measuring these lines, the weight of the atom, or isotope, can be determined. Using one of these instruments, it was found that neon gas, as it occurs in nature, consists of a mixture of two isotopes, one with an atomic weight of 20 (Ne^{20}) and the other with an atomic weight of 22 (Ne^{22}). The lighter isotope was ten times more abundant than the heavier one, which is why the atomic weight of normal neon is 20.2.

The convention is to use the chemical symbol of the element and a superscript that is the nearest whole number to the isotope's measured weight. The superscript is known as the mass number. Very often a subscript is written to signify the atomic number of the element, which indicates its place in the Periodic Table and the number of protons in its nucleus. Thus, for neon with atomic number 10, the complete symbol would be $_{10}Ne^{20}$.

Some elements have only one isotope, as for example gold (Au^{197}), tantalum (Ta^{181}), beryllium (Be^9), fluorine (F^{19}) and manganese (Mn^{55}). Others have two, three or as many as ten isotopes. Tin, for example, has isotopes of mass 112, 114, 115, 116, 117, 118, 119, 120, 122 and 124. The relative abundance of the isotopes in any element is easily displayed in a mass spectrogram. The illustration shows six of cadmium's eight isotopes (masses 106 and 108 are too scarce to show up in this photograph).

An atom-weighing machine can do much more than just separate out the various isotopes of the elements. It can be

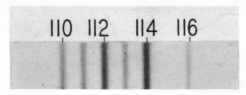

16. Isotopes of cadmium. The photograph
shows six of cadmium's eight isotopes as
registered in a mass spectrograph.

used to compare the weight of one isotope with the known
weight of another and thus let us deduce how much the unknown atom weighs. We have said before that the oxygen
standard is taken as 16.00000. At the time we did not define
any units for this weight. We now say that the weight of the
O^{16} isotope is taken as 16.00000 atomic mass units (amu).
This is our standard, and all other atoms are compared with it.

Precise comparisons of the weights of different isotopes can
be made by a number of techniques. For example, we can
measure the weight of carbon-12 by comparing the weight of
a carbon compound, methane or CH_4, with oxygen-16. Knowing the weight of hydrogen, we can deduce the weight of
carbon-12 by using the mass spectrograph to compare the
weights of the standard oxygen-16 atom and the CH_4 atom.
This is shown in illustration 17. A precision spectrograph
allows the two lines corresponding to oxygen and methane to
be measured accurately; as a result, by subtracting the known
weight of 4 hydrogen atoms, we arrive at the weight of car-
bon-12.

Highly accurate mass determinations have been made of
many of the 286 stable atoms that exist in nature. The precise
atomic weight of hydrogen, for instance, is not 1 but 1.008145;
nitrogen-14 has a mass of 14.00752, and oxygen-17 has an
exact atomic weight, or mass, of 17.00453 amu. Knowing that
helium-4 has a mass of 4.003879, we have precise masses for
all of the partners that are involved in Rutherford's disintegration of nitrogen. With our knowledge of the isotopes involved,

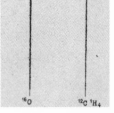

17. A mass spectrogram showing the two lines due to O^{16} and methane, CH_4. The separation between the two lines permits measurement of the mass of the CH_4 since O^{16} is taken as the standard. (Courtesy Professor J. Mattauch)

we can write an equation to represent the reaction which we illustrate graphically (see illustration):

$$_2He^4 \ + \ _7N^{14} \ = \ _8O^{17} \ + \ _1H^1$$

alpha   nitrogen   oxygen   proton
particle   nucleus   recoil

The mass number of 14 is assumed for nitrogen since this isotope constitutes 99.6 per cent of all nitrogen atoms. The superscripts on the left-hand side of the equation add up to 18, so that by subtracting 1 for the mass of the proton we arrive at 17 for the mass of the oxygen recoil nucleus. We assume, of course, that the mass numbers must add up to the same total on both sides of the equation, just as must the numbers denoting the electrical charge.

Now we shall go one step farther; we shall add up the exact masses of the partners on the left-hand side of the equa-

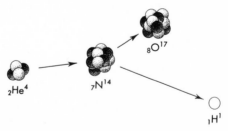

18. Schematic view of Rutherford's first nuclear disintegration. An alpha particle strikes a nucleus of nitrogen and ejects a high-speed proton. The resulting oxygen nucleus recoils from the impact.

tion and compare them with those for the end products on the right hand side of the equation.

$$\text{He}^4 = \ \ 4.003879 \text{ amu} \qquad \text{O}^{17} = 17.00453$$
$$\text{N}^{14} = 14.00752 \qquad\qquad \text{H}^1 \ = \ 1.008145$$
$$\text{He}^4 + \text{N}^{14} = \overline{18.01140} \text{ amu} \ ; \quad \text{O}^{17} + \text{H}^1 \ = \overline{18.01268} \ \text{ amu}$$

We see that the $\text{O}^{17} + \text{H}^1$ combination weighs more than the $\text{He}^4 + \text{N}^{14}$ by 0.00128 atomic mass units. This is at first a strange thing, since it appears that the nuclear reaction that took place when the alpha particle hit the nitrogen nucleus has created some mass—in violation of a basic law which states that matter and energy are conserved. It is here that Professor Einstein's $E = mc^2$ relation stands us in good stead. Using this mass energy relation we can show that a mass of 1 amu is equivalent to an energy of 931 million electron volts (1 amu = 931 Mev). Multiplying this figure by the 0.00128 of additional mass, we get a result of 1.2 Mev. We now state the meaning of this "excess" of energy on the right-hand side of the equation as follows: in order for this nuclear reaction to work, 1.2 Mev of energy has to be supplied by the alpha particle. In other words, it takes energy to make this nuclear reaction proceed. We shall see that in other nuclear reactions energy is liberated. In the case of the reaction that Rutherford observed, the energy is supplied in the form of the kinetic energy (energy of motion) of the fast-moving alpha particle.

Were it not for the relation between mass and energy we would be at a total loss to explain energy relations in nuclear reactions. A very dramatic illustration of the intimate relation between mass and energy is shown in the accompanying cloud chamber photograph. In this experiment X-rays strike the cloud chamber from the left. A very rare event takes place in the center of the chamber as the X-ray materializes into a pair of electrons. This process, called pair production, represents a complete conversion of energy (X-ray) into matter

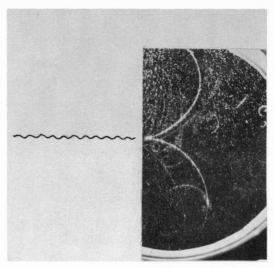

19. Cloud chamber photograph showing the production of a pair of electrons in the chamber gas. An X-ray entering from the left creates a pair of oppositely charged electrons, one of which curves upward and the other downward because of the magnetic field around the chamber.

(a pair of electrons); it occurs most frequently with high energy X-rays, for reasons we shall see presently. However, the event is only rarely observed in a gas, where there are few atoms present compared with those in a solid.

Before explaining the nature of this dramatic event, let us discuss briefly the behavior of electrons. If we aim a beam of X- or gamma rays at a cloud chamber equipped with a magnetic field, the usual cloud chamber picture will be something like the one shown in the accompanying illustration. In this case most of the electrons produced by the high-energy X-rays originate in the wall of the cloud chamber. The electrons leave a thin, sharp track in the cloud chamber and are curved into circles by the action of the magnetic field. The weaker in energy they are, the smaller is the circle into which they are

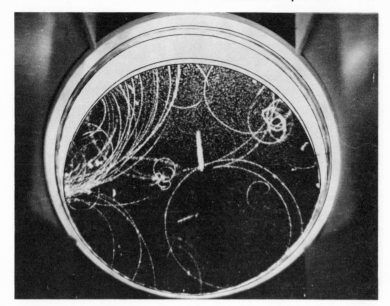

20. Gamma rays striking the side of the cloud chamber wall produce electrons which are curved into circular arcs by the action of a magnetic field. (Dr. James Phillips)

bent. We observe that the electrons bend in two directions, upward or downward, according to whether they are positive or negative in electrical charge. The electrons that are bent upward are negative in charge and those that are deflected downward are positive in charge.

The fact that there is a positive electron may be rather confusing at first, for up until now we have been talking as if all electrons were negatively charged. However, the negative electron has an alter ego—a positively charged twin that is the same in weight and in other respects, but differs in having a positive charge of electricity rather than a negative one. The amount of electrical charge is the same; it differs only in its sign, being plus rather than minus. This positively charged electron is called a positron. The positron is rather an uncommon twin, for it does not ordinarily exist in nature; it has to be created in a nuclear process. For example, when an energetic gamma or X-ray strikes matter, it may "disappear" and form a pair of electrons, one an ordinary electron and the other a positron. This dramatic process is illustrated in the cloud chamber picture that we referred to above. In this picture the gamma ray, entering from the left (naturally, it is not visible since, consisting of negative particles, it does not produce an ionizing path and consequently no water droplets can form on its trail), suddenly spawns a pair of oppositely divergent particle tracks. This striking photograph actually shows the creation of two particles (matter) from energy (a gamma ray). We say that the electrons materialize from the energy.

We have already indicated that the electron is small in weight compared with the mass of a proton. The electron's mass is known to be 0.00055 amu, which corresponds to an energy of 0.51 Mev. Therefore if a gamma ray creates a pair of electrons, it must furnish twice this energy, i.e., 1.02 Mev. Any additional energy supplied by the gamma ray goes into the motion of the electrons. Experimentally, it is observed that gamma rays below a million volts in energy do not produce pairs of electrons whereas those above this critical value do.

Is there any inverse process in which matter is converted into energy? Yes, the positron turns out to be very short-lived; when it slows down and comes close to a negative electron it may annihilate itself and the electron. When this happens, the electron pair disappears and is converted into gamma radiation. These creation and annihilation processes are striking examples of the interconvertibility of mass and energy. They present unassailable evidence of the validity of Dr. Einstein's $E = mc^2$.

8▫

Nuclear Architecture

THE news of Rutherford's splintering of the atom was not quite so sensational as Roentgen's discovery of X-rays. Nonetheless, word of the atom-smashing reached the public and people speculated about the meaning of this latest development in the research laboratory. They even wrote letters to Lord Rutherford predicting that dire catastrophe would ensue as a result of man's tinkering with atoms. He brushed aside these notions as nonsense—an attitude he maintained throughout his life. He did not think his researches would be of much general concern.

However, one of Rutherford's contemporaries, the famed astronomer, Arthur Eddington, stated that there is a "sub-atomic energy which, it is known, exists abundantly in all matter. We sometimes dream that man will one day learn to release it and use it for his service." This prophecy, made in the early 1920s, seemed farfetched then, for physicists still had only a faint inkling of what the nucleus was like.

They knew, to be sure, that the nucleus was very tiny compared with the atom itself. They knew that it was positively charged and contained as many positively charged protons as there were electrons in the rest of the atom. They knew, by virtue of Rutherford's brilliant researches, that the nucleus was not invulnerable; it could be splintered and part of it dislodged. But beyond this they had only primitive and inadequate knowledge. They knew nothing of the internal arrangement or the nature of the particles inside the nucleus; how they stuck together or why certain nuclei were stable and others were not. They were standing on the threshold of knowledge, and their appetites were whetted to peer more deeply into what took place inside the citadel of the atom.

The nature of the nucleus fascinated Rutherford, and early in his studies he speculated: "No doubt the positively charged center (nucleus) of the atom is a complicated system in movement, consisting in part of charged helium and hydrogen atoms (ions)." He drew the inference that the nucleus must contain helium ions from the fact that radioactive atoms emitted alpha particles. Referring to the protons in the nuclear core, he wrote: "It would appear as if the positively charged atoms of matter attract one another at very small distance, for otherwise it is difficult to see how the component parts at the center are held together."

Earlier we mentioned that four particles stick together to form an alpha particle—the nucleus of a helium atom. (Two of these, of course, are the positively charged protons. The exact nature of the other two particles, the neutrons as we have said, was not then known.) How does one explain the fact that such a system holds together at all? The two neutrons are electrically neutral, whereas the two protons are positively charged and, as we know, like charges repel each other. If purely electrical forces are all that are involved, the alpha particle—and every other nucleus—should blow itself to pieces. This was the great dilemma that faced scientists at the time of Rutherford's success in smashing the atom. It is still a great dilemma today, although now scientists have acquired a vaster store of information about the nucleus and its behavior. Common sense requires that the neutrons and protons must be glued together by some short-range, attracting force. We shall call this a nuclear force.

Nuclear forces, then, must be responsible for the fact that particles bind themselves together inside the nucleus. Let us examine a few of the simplest nuclei to see something of the nature of this binding. As we know, hydrogen (H^1)—sometimes called protium—is the lightest atom; it has an atomic weight of 1.008145 and a positive charge on its nucleus, which alone of all atomic nuclei consists of a single particle, a proton. The weight of this particular atom is ascertained with a precision comparable to weighing a person to the accuracy of the weight of a single postage stamp. The next most complex atom is an isotope of hydrogen called heavy hydrogen or deuterium. Deuterium occurs in nature to the amount of 1 part for every 5,000 parts of ordinary hydrogen. Its differs from its lighter cousin by having two particles in its nucleus. One of these, of course, is a proton; the other is a neutron, the nature of which we shall discuss in the next chapter. The atomic weight of the neutron is known to be 1.008985. We should now be able to determine the weight (or mass) of the deuterium atom by adding these two masses; the result is 2.017130 amu.

How does this calculated weight of the deuterium atom compare with its actual weight as measured in a mass spectrograph? It turns out that the measured mass is 2.014740 amu or 0.00239 atomic mass units *less* than we calculated it would be when we added the individual atomic weights of its proton and neutron. Clearly, some mass has been "lost" in putting the heavy hydrogen atom together.

Using Professor Einstein's $E = mc^2$ we can convert this "lost" mass into energy. Since 1 amu $= 931$ Mev, we see that the energy involved here amounts to 2.22 Mev. This is the binding energy with which the neutron and proton are glued together inside the nucleus of heavy hydrogen. When a free neutron and a free proton are fused, it is observed that gamma rays are emitted. This is the conversion of mass into energy. On the other hand, when a gamma ray bombards a nucleus of heavy hydrogen, the hydrogen nucleus can be split into a neutron and a proton provided that the gamma ray has energy exceeding 2.22 Mev. This is the reverse process—the conversion of energy into mass, for as we have seen, the atomic weight of the two separate particles into which the heavy hydrogen or deuterium nucleus·splits is greater than the atomic weight of the unsplit nucleus.

One way of looking at the synthesis and break-up of a deuterium nucleus is to imagine that when a neutron or proton exists inside the nucleus it is abnormal, having lost some of its normal mass. When energy equivalent to this "lost" mass is again supplied to the nuclear constituents they regain their full weight and are independent particles no longer clinging to one another.

We can make the same calculations, adding up the masses of the neutrons and protons, for helium-4. It turns out that the sum of the individual atomic weights of its two neutrons and two protons is 0.0303 amu heavier than the measured mass of He^4 which is 4.00280. Again using Einstein's formula of $E = mc^2$, the lost difference in mass is equal to 28.2 million electron volts of energy. This means that this particular combination of neutrons and protons is tightly bound and therefore the helium nucleus, or alpha particle, is an exceedingly stable particle. To knock it apart would take 28.2 Mev of energy.

As we examine more complex and heavier atoms, we find that the total binding energy of the nucleus increases. For magnesium the binding energy is about 200 Mev and for uranium it is 1,800 Mev. If you could shatter a uranium nucleus into its 238 neutrons and protons you would release 1.8 billion electron volts of energy. As everyone knows, the uranium atom has been split into two fragments by a process called nuclear fission (Chapter 10). In the fission process we can tap only a fraction of the binding energy of the nucleus— in fact, only the difference between the binding energies of the two separate fragments and the total binding energy of the uranium nucleus before it was split. This last amounts to 1,800 Mev, whereas for an atom of mass 119 the total binding energy is 1,000 Mev. Since there are two fragments, the total binding energy is 2,000 Mev. The energy released in fission is therefore 2,000 — 1,800 or 200 Mev. This energy is made available because the very unstable uranium nucleus splits into two more stable fragments. This is anticipating the story of fission, but it is useful to see now why and how energy is released in such nuclear processes.

Most atoms have nuclei in which the constituents are bound together with about the same average energy, that is, each neutron and proton sticks to the nucleus with a binding energy of between 7 and 8 Mev. This can be explained if we think of the nucleus as a very compact aggregate of particles. We may even assume that the nucleus behaves like a very dense liquid. Using this model, we can describe a nucleus as having a radius that increases slowly as the atoms get heavier and heavier. The heaviest nuclei, such as uranium, are about five times as wide as the lightest nuclei. The nuclear radius can be measured or deduced by a number of techniques, and it turns out that the radius of a very heavy nucleus, such as gold ($_{72}Au^{107}$), which contains 72 protons and 107 neutrons, is about one-trillionth of a centimeter.

If even such a heavy nucleus is so tiny and yet, like all nuclei, contains 99.95 per cent of the atom's weight, it follows that it must be exceedingly dense. One can calculate that nuclei have a density that is one hundred trillion times the density of water. If the planet earth were to be collapsed to its nuclear dimensions—i.e., shrunk so that all its atoms were stripped of their electrons and were replaced with nuclei packed edge to edge, our earth would be a sphere two hundred yards in diameter.

Rutherford and his contemporaries knew full well that they had limited power with which to bombard the nucleus and discover its secrets. Naturally radioactive substances offered the means of bombardment, and the alpha particle was their main bullet. What they wanted and needed was some man-made, controllable device with which to attack the atom.

Sir John Cockcroft and E. T. Walton were the first to develop a machine for artificially producing high-speed atomic particles. In 1929 they succeeded in making a new type of

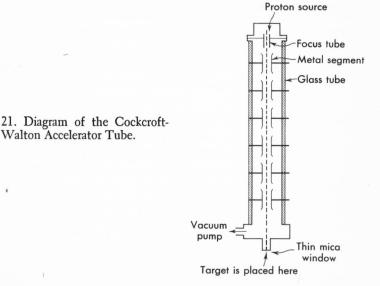

21. Diagram of the Cockcroft-Walton Accelerator Tube.

high-voltage source capable of generating an output of hundreds of thousands of volts. Having done this, they needed two things to complete their apparatus. First, they needed a source of atomic particles. This they obtained by devising an electric arc to ionize atoms of hydrogen gas, thus producing protons. In the proton the physicists had a new and more versatile weapon with which to assault the atom. Next, they needed some mechanism with which to accelerate these protons to high speed. They built a long glass tube which was continuously pumped free of air. The proton source was located at the top of this accelerating tube, as shown in the diagram. Inside the glass tube they lined up a series of metal cylinders each of which was connected to a high-voltage lead sealed in through the side of the main tube.

The Cockcroft-Walton accelerator works as follows: protons produced at the top of the tube are "focused" to form a beam of particles moving down along the axis of the tube through the hollow metal cylinders. This beam of charged particles is attracted into the first metal cylinder by the high voltage imposed on it, and they pick up speed. As the protons emerge from the first cylinder segment, they are again hurled downward by the additional voltage on the second cylinder, and so on until they reach the last cylinder segment at the bottom of the accelerator. Here they strike a "target," in which nuclear reactions can be studied. The two British scientists were able to control the energy of the proton beam by adjusting the voltage applied to the accelerator tube. In this way they could study the action of protons at 100,000 volts through a range up to 400,000 volts.

As their first target Cockcroft and Walton chose the light element lithium ($_3Li^7$). The proton beam emerging from the apparatus through a very thin mica window was very weak and could penetrate only to a distance of about one centimeter in air. Despite this drawback the experimenters were hopeful that they might observe some reaction. However, they were astonished to find that their lithium target became a source of long-range ionizing particles. Cloud chamber photographs by Walton and an associate revealed a dramatic splitting of the lithium nucleus into two halves. The illustration shows a number of these lithium fissions, all of which represent speedy alpha particles. The nuclear reaction for this lithium bombardment is written:

$$_1H^1 + _3Li^7 = _2He^4 + _2He^4$$
proton + lithium = alpha particle + alpha particle

We again use our knowledge of atomic masses to calculate the energy involved in this reaction. It turns out that the sum of the masses of the alpha particles is 0.0186 fewer mass units than the proton plus lithium combination. This "lost" mass, when multiplied by 931 Mev, is equal to 17.32 Mev. Since there are two particles, each alpha particle must carry off 8.67 Mev of energy. Measurements of the range of the alpha particles agree very closely with this predicted energy.

The astonishing aspect of the first man-made, artificial disintegration of the lithium nucleus was the fact that it was accomplished with such puny atomic projectiles. Cockcroft and Walton must have felt like big-game hunters who bagged a huge beast with a small-caliber gun. Using a beam of proton bullets with only a fraction of 1 Mev of energy, the two scientists had caused the lithium nucleus to release over 17 Mev of energy. People could be forgiven if they speculated about making use of this nuclear reaction in a practical way. The fly in the ointment was that Cockcroft and Walton put more energy into their machine than they could ever get out of it from the lithium reaction. Only a few out of a million protons produced a reaction, and the energy involved in producing the protons was far greater than that released by the speedy alpha particles.

Cockcroft and Walton had happened to choose a target atom that was ideally mated to their proton projectile. Other elements would not have given them such a neat, observable result as the production of fast-moving alpha particles. The fact that low-energy protons could split a nucleus of lithium caused many scientists to revise their ideas about the nucleus.

Many had thought that such a weak proton would be repelled by the positive charge on the lithium nucleus and would not get to first base, whereas some of the protons scored home runs. The proton had obviously found a weak point in the defenses of the lithium nucleus and had managed to get around the barrier of electrical repulsion. According to previous concepts, this would have been impossible since, as we have said, the rampart of the lithium nucleus presents a high positively charged barrier which could not be surmounted by such a weak proton.

However, revolutionary developments in theoretical physics, coming just before the Cockcroft-Walton experiment, pointed to a new concept of the nuclear barrier. This theory had explained what had previously baffled everyone—the emission of alpha particles from the nuclei of heavy elements. According to earlier ideas, the alpha particle should be a permanent prisoner inside the confines of the nucleus. The energy of the alpha particle should be insufficient to allow it to hurdle the electrical barrier around the nucleus and emerge.

In 1926 Erwin Schrödinger, Austrian-born physicist, broke the ground for the science of wave mechanics, which was to revolutionize physics. His new theory put emphasis upon the wave properties of matter and it was successful in explaining previously unsolved problems of atomic structure. A trio of scientists, one of them working independently, applied the new science to the problem of alpha particle emission. R. W. Gurney, an English scientist working in collaboration with Edward U. Condon of the United States—and George Gamow, a Russian-born theoretician—developed a mathematical approach which explained alpha emission from nuclei. Agreeing that alpha particles could never get over the high top of the nuclear barrier, they assumed that, instead, the particles "tunneled" or "leaked" through the barrier by virtue of their wave properties.

We may explain how the weak proton manages to get inside the lithium nucleus by reversing the process of alpha particle emission. If a charged particle can leak out of a nucleus, then turn about should be fair play and it should be possible for a charged particle to leak or wriggle into the nucleus. This is what happens in the case of the proton. The lithium nucleus happens to have a chink in its armor that makes it quite vulnerable to attack with low-energy protons. Data gained from the proton bombardment of lithium tells us a good deal about how the neutrons and protons are arranged inside the lithium nucleus. We cannot pursue this point much farther without getting quite complicated; it is sufficient to say that experiments with nuclear bombardment reveal much about what happens inside the nucleus and gives valuable clues to the dark interior of this most complex heart of matter.

The Fateful Bullet

NEITHER the proton nor the alpha particle was destined to be the Open Sesame to the domain of atomic energy. Yet another kind of bullet—the neutron—was to lead to the release of atomic energy on a practical scale.

The neutron was discovered in 1932 by Sir James Chadwick at Cambridge University in the course of repeating an experiment that had been started two years earlier by two Germans, Walther Bothe and H. Becker. They had found that when alpha particles from polonium bombarded a light element, preferably beryllium, a very penetrating ray was produced. Following up this lead, Irène Curie (daughter of the discoverers of radium) and her husband, Frédéric Joliot-Curie, observed that this penetrating radiation could, in turn, knock energetic protons out of the atoms of a hydrogen-rich substance such as paraffin.

Chadwick decided to examine this penetrating beryllium radiation with the aid of a nitrogen-filled cloud chamber to see if he could find some clue to the nature of the puzzling ray. He soon found that only single tracks showed up within the gas of the chamber. These he thought must be speedy nitrogen nuclei produced by and recoiling from a billiard-ball-like collision with the strange ray. Two partners were necessary for the collision—the nitrogen atom and the still unidentified ray emitted by the beryllium—but only one, the nitrogen nucleus, showed up in the chamber. The penetrating radiation did not produce ions and therefore left no visible track. This meant that it did not have an electrical charge. But more than that, he realized, it had to be a fairly heavy particle, not just a powerful gamma ray, in order to knock the nitrogen atoms about with such force. By studying the trajectories of the nitrogen recoils in the chamber, Chadwick was able to deduce that the mass of the particle must be about the same as that of a hydrogen atom. He called the new particle the neutron. His discovery came a decade after Rutherford had predicted that such a particle must be a fundamental building stone of all nuclei.

The Joliot-Curies, who had come so close to making this great discovery, continued their research and made an equally important finding. They found that when alpha particles bombarded light elements, particularly aluminum, positrons were emitted. But what really astonished the two investigators was that the irradiated aluminum foil continued to emit positrons even after the source of the alpha particles was removed. It was evident that the aluminum foil had been made artificially radioactive. This radioactivity decreased quickly, but in the same manner as a naturally radioactive substance. We can explain the production of the new radioelement by writing down the equations for the nuclear reaction:

$$_{13}Al^{27} + {_2}He^4 = {_{15}}P^{30} + {_0}n^1$$
$$(neutron)$$

The identity of the new isotope is determined since it was established experimentally that neutrons were produced by the reaction. This being the case, we add up the atomic numbers on the left-hand side of the equation and find $13 + 2 = 15$, which must then be the atomic number for the residual atom since the neutron has 0 as its atomic number. The number 15 corresponds to the element phosphorus in the Periodic Table. The mass number is obtained by adding $27 + 4 = 31$ and subtracting 1 for the neutron to give 30. Thus the new radioactive species which the Joliot-Curies produced is P^{30} or phosphorus-30.

Natural phosphorus consists of a single isotope of mass 31; therefore, the new species of phosphorus is an isotope that differs from the naturally occurring isotope of phosphorus by having a one less neutron in its nucleus. The abnormal P^{30} is unstable and disintegrates by emitting a positron, as indicated by the following equation:

$$_{15}P^{30} = {}_{14}Si^{30} + {}_{+1}e^{0}$$
$$\text{(positron)}$$

The effect of emitting a positron is to change phosphorus into silicon. This occurs rather quickly since phosphorus-30 has a half-life of 2½ minutes. The silicon atom that results is stable—i.e., does not disintegrate further. Isotopes that are artificially made radioactive are usually called radioisotopes. Hundreds of new radioisotopes were discovered within a short time after the birth of artificial radioactivity in 1934. It was also found that other particles besides the alpha ray were effective in producing radioisotopes.

Neutrons were found to induce radioactivity in some elements, and at this point we introduce the man who was to become the master of the neutron. Enrico Fermi, a young Italian theoretical physicist, switched his attention from theory to experiment when he heard of the twin impact of the neutron and artificial radioactivity. Within a short time Fermi gathered together a group of young Italians, many of whom were to become famous in their own right. Together they started a systematic irradiation of all the elements. In the course of their experiments they made the remarkable observation that almost all atoms can capture neutrons, but that this process is more effective if the neutrons are reduced in energy. Since the neutron has no nuclear charge it can slip through the atom's electrical defenses with the greatest of ease; this was understandable, but why should the neutrons be absorbed by nuclei more easily when the neutrons had lost most of their energy? Why should slow neutrons be more effective in making nuclei radioactive than fast ones?

The answer to these questions is to be found in the wave nature of the neutron. Although it may appear as a tiny, hard blob of matter without electrical charge, the neutron does have wave properties and as a consequence it can be described as having a certain wave length. Its wave length depends upon its energy; the greater its energy, the faster it travels, and the faster it travels, the shorter its wave length is. So, as the neutron slows down it increases in wave length. (It may help you to understand the relation between wave length and speed if you have seen a snake moving across the ground. When it is traveling quickly, it looks something like this ∿∿∿ ; when moving slowly and sluggishly, perhaps after a full meal, it looks more like this ⌒‿⌒‿. The crests of its undulations are further apart than when it is moving rapidly.) Because of its wave nature, the free neutron has a greater chance of interacting with—or wriggling into—and being captured by a nucleus when it slows down—a far greater chance than have charged particles. Indeed, it is the rare neutron that does not get captured by a nucleus once it is released.

Neutrons such as are produced by the impact of alpha particles upon a light element are born with high energy. If in turn these fast-moving neutrons are allowed to bump up against light atoms, such as hydrogen, beryllium and carbon, they are readily slowed down. Each impact robs them of a little energy. We say that such elements act as moderators to reduce the speed of the neutrons. Elements such as boron, although light, are unsuitable as slowing-down agents since they have a very great tendency to capture neutrons permanently rather than merely bounce them around.

Among the various elements that Fermi exposed to a bath of slow neutrons was the last one in the Periodic System—element 92, uranium. One day in the spring of 1934 Fermi bombarded a lump of uranium with neutrons and found that the element, like many others, became very radioactive. This, in itself, was not unusual, but Fermi was puzzled by the fact that four different radioactive species of atoms were formed by the bombardment. At least he could identify beta particles corresponding to four different half-lives. It seemed logical to assign one of the activities to U^{239}, produced by the simple capture of a neutron by U^{238}, as illustrated by the equation $_{92}U^{238} + _{0}n^{1} = _{92}U^{239}$. If the U^{239} isotope then emitted a negatively charged beta particle, the following equation must hold:

$$_{92}U^{239} = _{93}X^{239} + _{-1}e^{0}$$

where X is the element formed by the disintegration of U^{239}. When an atom loses a negative charge (in this case a beta particle) it is the same as gaining a positive charge. Thus the atomic number 92 must be increased by 1 unit because of the −1 unit required for the negative electron. This meant that X would be the symbol for a new transuranium element, i.e., an element lying beyond uranium in the periodic system. This was very exciting; one could even speculate that element 93 would be unstable and disintegrate to form an isotope of element 94.

In the June 16, 1934, issue of *Nature*, a British scientific magazine, Fermi published a paper titled "Possible Production of Elements of Atomic Number Higher than 92." In this paper Fermi singled out element 93 but also speculated on 94 and 95. Scientists all over the world were stimulated by the announcement of possible man-made new elements. In the United States, France, Britain, Switzerland and other nations, scientists set to work on experiments designed to repeat and extend Fermi's research. For almost five years the work went on and during this time scientists felt sure that they had not only confirmed Fermi's production of element 93 but that they had gone farther and found additional transuranium elements.

Then in December of 1939 two German scientists, Otto Hahn and Fritz Strassmann, performed a critical experiment which was ultimately to change man's way of life. Repeating the Fermi research in their laboratory at the Kaiser Wilhelm Institute in the residential suburbs of Berlin, they bombarded a sample of uranium with neutrons. They then began a series of maneuvers to separate and identify by chemical means the various radioactive elements from the uranium. They had done similar work for many months, during which time they thought that they had identified elements ranging from atomic number 88 up to 96. They concentrated on analyzing that fraction of their separated material which they thought contained small amounts of radium (88), actinium (89) and thorium (90).

Much to their surprise, Hahn and Strassmann discovered that their sample contained barium—a middle-weight element of atomic number 56! How in the world could neutron impact upon uranium produce detectable amounts of an element halfway down the Periodic Table from element 92? It was almost as though the atom had been split in half. In a letter to the editor of the German scientific periodical *Naturwissenschaften*, the two researchers wrote on December 22, 1938, of their findings. They even pointed out that if barium had an isotope of mass 138, then the other atom produced by the neutron's collision with uranium-238 must be manganese-101 (although they had not detected the latter).

Yet in the face of their evidence, the two Germans were cautious—perhaps out of respect for the many eminent scientists whose steps they had retraced, but more likely because they found it incredible that the uranium atom could be smashed asunder. Whatever the reasons, they published the experimental findings without emphasizing any conclusion and then settled back to think about their research.

Professor Hahn later wrote: "Our overcautiousness stemmed primarily from the fact that as chemists we hesitated to announce a revolutionary discovery in physics. Nevertheless we did speak of the 'bursting' of uranium, as we called the surprising process that had yielded barium, far down in the periodic table."

They had communicated their findings, prior to publication, to their old friend and co-worker who had been driven out of Nazi Germany by Hitler's intolerance, Lise Meitner. In Sweden the Austrian-born physicist, with her nephew, Otto Frisch, a distinguished physicist from Niels Bohr's laboratory in Copenhagen, analyzed the Hahn-Strassmann experimental results. They became convinced that the atom had in fact been split and they set about to prove and explain this radical new nuclear process.

First, to explain the new phenomenon, Lise Meitner made mathematical calculations based upon a model of the uranium nucleus that assumed that the aggregate of 238 particles behaved as a little drop of liquid. When struck by a neutron this droplet should begin to oscillate and it might be sufficiently agitated so that the neutrons and protons would be set into mortal conflict. Eventually the battle would distend the nucleus into a dumbbell shape and the charged protons would force the ends of the dumbbell farther and farther apart. Finally, although the times involved were measured in trillionths of a second, the tenuous link holding the two parts together would snap and the fragments would fly apart. To use the language contributed by Dr. Frisch, the uranium nucleus would be fissioned.

Second, to verify the reality of the nuclear fission, Otto Frisch hurried to Denmark from his Christmas holiday in Sweden and proceeded to throw together apparatus to record the fast-flying fragments of the uranium atom. It was expected on the basis of the atomic masses of the fragments as compared with the mass of the uranium atom that nuclear fission should set free energy equivalent to 0.21 atomic mass units—i.e., about 200 Mev of energy. This fission energy should appear in the form of the energy of motion of the uranium fragments. Since they would be highly charged particles, Frisch knew that their electrical impulses might be registered by means of an ion chamber. He quickly verified the fact that such atomic fragments are indeed produced in uranium fission.

Both theory and experiment put fission on a solid basis, so that there could be no doubt about the new phenomenon. We have already explained that the uranium atom splits into two more stable middle-weight atoms, and that it is the difference between the binding energy of the uranium atom and the combined binding energies of the two fragments that is released in fission. It is important to note that in the fission process the total number of neutrons and protons remains unchanged. What happens is that they are rearranged from a single nucleus with 238 particles into two nuclei whose neutrons and protons add up to the same number. The total energy associated with the entire mass of the uranium atom amounts, as we have seen earlier, to 238 x 931 Mev or 220,000 Mev. This is the energy that would be released if all the mass of all of its neutrons and protons were totally converted into energy. In fission we get only the reshuffling energy of the neutron and proton combinations and this is only 200 Mev or 0.1 per cent of the vast mass-energy of the uranium nucleus. However, we have already calculated that the mass-energy of one pound of matter is about 10,000,000 tons of TNT. So even if one could only tap one-tenth of one per cent of this amount, it would still add up to 10,000 tons of TNT for a pound of uranium.

Dramatic proof of the splitting of the uranium atom is supplied by the cloud chamber photograph. The Danish physicist J. K. Bøggild stretched a thin foil of gold across the center of a cloud chamber and deposited a thin layer of uranium on this foil. Then he directed a beam of neutrons on the uranium and photographed the tracks of particles in the chamber. He succeeded in catching a number of uranium atoms in the act of fission. In the photograph the central horizontal white line represents the uranium film, and the two dense tracks that streak out from the foil are uranium fragments. The short spurs jutting off from the end of the track give the appearance of a Christmas tree.

The uranium nucleus is rather perverse and does not often split into two equal pieces. Rather, it prefers to fission into a wide variety of pairs of fragments. Each pair, however, always adds up to the original mass of the uranium atom. Analysis of the distance that uranium fragments travel in air shows that they fall into two groups: a light group that travels about one inch, and a heavy group with a range of about 0.8 inch.

At this point some additional information about the nature of uranium is necessary for a clear understanding of the splitting of the uranium atom. Using a mass spectrograph, Professor A. J. Dempster of the University of Chicago had analyzed the composition of natural uranium and discovered that whereas uranium had been thought to consist solely of U^{238} atoms, there were some lighter isotopes. He found that an isotope 3 units lighter in mass, U^{235}, is present to the extent of one part of the U^{235} to 140 parts of the U^{238}. In other words, natural uranium was 99.3 per cent U^{238} and 0.7 per cent U^{235}.

As it happens, it is the scarce, light isotope of uranium that fissions most easily. Therefore, in writing down the equations for the fission process we shall use the U^{235} nucleus rather than the heavier nucleus. We represent fission as follows:

22. Cloud chamber photograph showing the two recoiling fragments emitted by a fissioning uranium nucleus. The longer (lower) track corresponds to the lighter fragment. A gold foil covered with film of uranium is stretched across the chamber. (Courtesy Professor J. K. Bøggild)

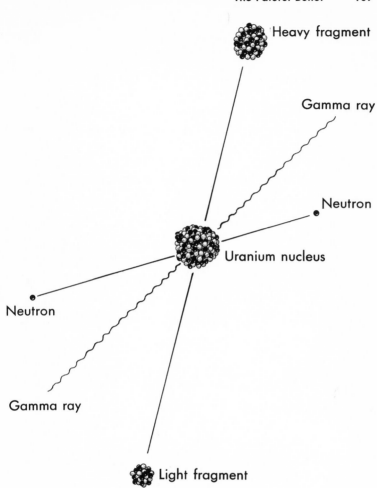

23. Schematic diagram showing fission of a uranium nucleus into two fragments.

$$U^{235} + n^1 = La^{139} + Mo^{95} + 2\,n^1$$
uranium+neutron=lanthanum+molybdenum+neutrons

This is but one of many ways by which the uranium nucleus splits, but it is a rather probable way. If we add up the masses of the particles involved, we get on the left of the equation

235.124 + 1.009 = 236.133; whereas on the right the sum is 138.955 + 94.945 + 2.018 = 235.918. The loss in mass of 0.215 amu corresponds to about 200 Mev.

We shall by-pass for the time being the fact that 2 additional neutrons are born in the fission process and will return to this important point in the next chapter. Let us look at what, at first, appears to be a real error in writing the fission equation. A glance at the Periodic Table shows that the element lanthanum has atomic number 57, and that for molybdenum is 42; these add up to 99 and not 92, the atomic number of uranium. The explanation of the discrepancy is that the fission process by which the pair of lanthanum-molybdenum nuclei are born does not produce these two atoms at the time of fission. They are the stable end products of a radioactive series which, in the case of the lanthanum atom, begins with iodine, which is element 53. The radioiodine emits a beta particle (thus gaining a positive charge) to form an atom of xenon and this decays to an atom of cesium (atomic number 55). Both decays occur quickly and then cesium disintegrates with a half-life of ten minutes to form an isotope of barium, which in turn decays with a half-life of eighty-five minutes to form the stable lanthanum-139. Looking back, we see that since the fission fragment born at the time of fission had an atomic number of 53, its other partner must have had 92 — 53 or 39. (Element 39 is yttrium.)

All in all, there are over a hundred separate fission products of appreciable half-life and many more very short-lived isotopes. They range from zinc through the rare earths up to europium, covering a span of 33 atomic numbers. The mass numbers of the isotopes run from 72 to 156, but the isotopes that are produced most abundantly cluster around masses 95 and 139. Some of the fission fragments are long-lived; for example, strontium-90 has a half-life of twenty-eight years, cesium-137 about thirty years, cerium-144 about one year.

This in part helps to explain why the scientists were rather confused when they attempted to analyze the results of bombarding uranium with neutrons. Although they did not know it, they were dealing with a mess of fission products with widely varying half-lives. These were mistaken for transuranium elements and put the investigators off the trail. But part of the reason why the scientists failed to discover fission for so many years was that they did not believe that such a cataclysmic convulsion of the nucleus could take place.

10[□]

Uranium Energy

NEWS of the atom-splitting in Germany spread like wildfire to the laboratories of many nations even before publication of the Hahn-Strassmann paper or Lise Meitner's explanation of fission appeared in print. One man to whom the news was to be of overwhelming importance was the stocky Italian physicist, Enrico Fermi. He had just arrived in the United States and had begun his research at Columbia University when he heard by word of mouth about uranium fission. Fermi knew in an instant that what he had thought were transuranium elements had undoubtedly been fission products of uranium.

Fermi also knew that the splitting of the uranium atom did not necessarily mean that nuclear fission would be a practical source of energy. In an experiment neutrons might fission a million uranium atoms, but this did not yield an impressive amount of energy—only enough to sustain a fly in a moment's flight. But the real trouble with the experiments was that they took a vastly greater input of energy than they released in output of fission energy. Fermi knew that if fission were to be of any practical importance there would have to be a self-sustaining reaction. In other words, fission would have to produce further fission and so on in a chain sequence of reactions, so that energy could build up. But how could one fission of a uranium nucleus produce such a chain reaction?

The clue to this puzzler is the neutron, because this is the particle that causes fission. Therefore, if there were to be a chain reaction in uranium, fission would have to produce neutrons. Fermi reasoned that this was not too improbable, since fission was such a violent, disruptive process. Neutrons might be shot out from the fissioning nucleus or they might be emitted by the fragments produced by fission. In any event, Fermi felt that the fission process might well produce neutrons from the ruptured nucleus, and he began experiments to see if his speculation was correct.

Uranium, lots of uranium, was necessary for even these early experiments. As soon as the research gave promise of success, and was financed by the government, even larger quantities of the key element were required. At first the uranium came from Canada; then during the war this initial flow of the atomic material was swelled by the output of the fabulous Shinkolobwe mines deep in the heart of the Belgian Congo. These mines, first discovered during World War I by a prospector looking for silver, consisted of thick veins of lustrous pitchblende which outcropped on the surface. Because of the very high concentration of uranium, running over 60 per cent of the mineral's content, these deposits were the only mother lode of uranium ore known. After World War I they had been used as a source of radium when the price of that element was boosted to three million dollars an ounce. However, at the outbreak of Hitler's rampages in Europe the Shinkolobwe mines had been shut down. They were reopened when the need for uranium as an atomic energy material became apparent.

Fermi began his research with a few hundred pounds of uranium that was not very pure. His main purpose was to find out whether neutrons were given off when the uranium nu-

cleus was split, and if so, how many. The whole feasibility
of atomic energy balanced upon the experiments that Fermi
and his associates performed on the campus of Columbia
University, not too many miles removed from downtown
Manhattan. The heart of New York City, throbbing with its
daily pulse of millions of people, was unaware of the quiet
work of a few men in a university laboratory. They soon
proved that, as Fermi had thought likely, neutrons were
emitted when uranium was bombarded with neutrons, and
they then tackled the job of finding out how many neutrons
were ejected from a single uranium nucleus when it split.

The whole future of atomic energy depended upon this
single number—a vital nuclear statistic—for if the average
number were too small, say much less than two, it would not

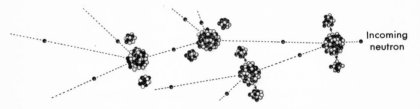

Incoming
neutron

24. Illustrating the chain reaction in uranium. Neutron coming in
from the right strikes uranium nucleus, splitting it into two fragments.
Two neutrons are released and these strike two other uranium nuclei,
releasing a total of five neutrons. In this way the chain reaction builds
up.

be possible to achieve a chain reaction in uranium. If fewer
than an average two neutrons were emitted per fission, then,
in any attempt to make a self-sustaining neutron-fission reaction, there would be the problem of preventing the neutrons
from escaping without first striking uranium nuclei. If the
neutrons flew off into space they would be "lost" from the
system. Just to maintain the chain reaction, at least one neutron released by each fission had to fission another uranium
nucleus. However, Fermi knew that impurities in uranium,
such as the light element boron, would gobble up stray neu-

trons and rob them from the chain reaction. He knew also that the 140-fold more abundant uranium-238 would capture neutrons without splitting. But even more serious was the fact that the slippery neutrons could flit through the mass of uranium and escape into space. It was for this reason that to set up a chain reaction, each fission of a uranium nucleus had to give birth to roughly two neutrons. Early measurements showed that the number was about 2.3 neutrons per fission, and later refinements gave a value of 2.5. Since there is no possibility of chopping a neutron in half, the value of 2.5 must be interpreted as an average in which many fissions yields two neutrons and others give off three neutrons. In any event, it looked as though there would be some surplus neutrons to allow for losses due to escape and capture.

Fermi was still a long way from proving that one could achieve a chain reaction in uranium. Things looked hopeful, to be sure, but no one knew how much pure uranium would have to be made for use in a chain reaction, or if such high-purity uranium could be produced. However, it was apparent to Fermi that you could not sustain a chain reaction in solid uranium. Too many of the neutrons would get absorbed in the abundant U^{238} nuclei without causing fission. Some way had to be found to circumvent this undesirable fate for the neutrons, and Fermi hit upon the idea of introducing a light element into a stack of uranium in order to slow down or moderate the speed of the neutrons. He reasoned that if he could bounce the neutrons around in a light element such as carbon, they would have a chance to escape capture in U^{238} and would, because of their lower speed, split U^{235} nuclei more readily.

His idea was to build up a great mass of carbon (graphite) and intersperse in it chunks of uranium. Neutrons produced in uranium fission would flash out and strike the carbon atoms and be bounced around without being captured, provided the carbon was very pure. In the process of being knocked about in the light element or moderator, the neutrons would lose energy and thus, as we explained earlier, be more capable of fissioning U^{235} and less likely to be swallowed up by U^{238}. Then when the now slow neutrons diffused back into the uranium after spending most of their life in the carbon they would fission U^{235} without much trouble and produce more neutrons to carry on the chain reaction.

How much uranium would you need? How much carbon? How pure would the materials have to be? No one knew the answers, but Fermi operated in a dual role as experimentalist and theoretician. One day he would be in the laboratory measuring neutron absorption in carbon and the next he would be calculating how many lumps of uranium would be required for a given amount of graphite. The calculations as to the proper or best size for the uranium lump and how the lumps should be spaced in a great mass of graphite were exceedingly difficult because of the many different factors that had to be considered.

As the researchers continued their experiments and their calculations, it became apparent that there were three formidable hurdles to achieving the chain reaction.

First, many tons of pure uranium would be needed. This was more than just a production problem; it was a major challenge to chemists and chemical engineers to perfect the means of purifying uranium to a degree not previously known even in the purification of other elements. Even tiny amounts of the vicious "cannibal" boron atom had to be eliminated. They even had to take precautions that workmen handling material did not use a boron-containing soap which might contaminate uranium or graphite.

Second, hundreds of tons of ultrapure graphite had to be produced. Graphite of the purity required was unheard of in the trade. Much work had to be done in order to develop techniques for refining graphite that would be free from dangerous impurities.

Third, more elaborate calculations had to be made and a new theory developed to predict how neutrons would behave inside various assemblies of graphite and uranium. New mathematical techniques had to be improvised for this problem and even then one had to be content with approximations.

Even with these problems licked, there was also the tricky task of "controlling" the chain reaction. It was decided to make use of the nasty elements that gobbled up so many neutrons from the chain reaction. Cadmium is one such neutron-hungry element, and it was agreed that a long rod of this metal would be placed within the graphite-uranium structure for control purposes, the idea being that when the rod was fully inserted it would absorb a lot of neutrons, whereas withdrawal of the rod would "release" neutrons to the chain reaction. Physicists calculated how much cadmium would be necessary to inhibit or stop a chain reaction completely so that there would be no possibility of a runaway chain reaction. And to be on the safe side, they allowed for additional safety-control rods which could be slammed into the structure should their calculations prove inadequate.

Fermi's original small group of workers had grown since he began his work in 1939 and late in 1942 a larger task force of scientists augmented these pioneers. Operations had been relocated on the campus of the University of Chicago, less than a mile from Lake Michigan on the South Side of Chicago.

On the afternoon of a cold winter's day, December 2, 1942, Fermi and two score of his colleagues came to a critical point in history. They assembled in an abandoned squash court adjoining the university's unused football field. Before them loomed a massive structure of black, greasy graphite in which were imbedded seven tons of uranium. The illustration shows how the nineteenth layer of graphite blocks looked, interspersed with uranium.

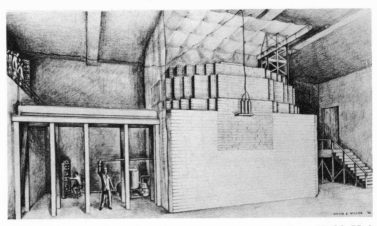

25. Sketch of the first self-sustaining chain reactor at Stagg Field, University of Chicago, December 2, 1942. Neutron counters are shown on the face of the pile and a physicist is shown withdrawing a control rod from the left face of the reactor. (U.S. Army)

The "silent monster," as one scientist nicknamed this pile of graphite, remained quiescent. Not even a faint pulse of a chain reaction throbbed within its interior, for Fermi took no chances—the cadmium control rods were fully inserted into the pile. At his signal, one of the control rods was slowly withdrawn from the pile of uranium and graphite. A trio of counters (shown on the side of the pile) recorded any neutrons that might be released. The neutrons required to start the chain reaction would come from the cosmic rays that bombard the earth constantly, or from the erratic, spontaneous fission of uranium.

Slowly, at first, the clicks of the counters became audible as neutrons started to build up within the machine. The silent machine was beginning to "tick." The control rod was pulled out six more inches, then a foot, and the counters increased their chant until there was a steady tempo as the neutrons came more rapidly, freed from the depressing action of the cadmium absorbers.

Fermi stood by the counting instruments, imperturbable,

26. Photograph made of the first reactor during assembly. The nineteenth layer of graphite was being added when the photograph was made in November of 1942. In all, some 37 layers were made in order to achieve criticality in this first chain reactor. (Argonne National Laboratory)

noting the instrument readings and converting them into split-second calculations on his slide rule. A calculation made, he would call for a new setting of the control rod. Then still another calculation and another setting. The atmosphere in the room grew tense. Success or failure? In the instrument readings and in Fermi's calculations would be found the answer.

Minutes ticked away as the control rods were shifted, instrument readings made and converted into calculations. Each time the counters took up a more frenzied pace. Finally, Fermi looked up from his slide rule and a smile creased his swarthy face as he announced calmly: "The chain reaction is self-sustaining." And with these words man crossed the threshold of the Atomic Age.

Fermi's success at Chicago was to pave the way for the construction of huge nuclear reactors which in turn would serve as prototypes of postwar nuclear power plants and atomic engines. The first self-sustaining chain reaction pointed toward more powerful devices for using uranium's energy. In all such devices, the energy of the recoil fragments of the uranium nucleus is converted into heat. This thermal energy is then extracted from the reactor core by circulating a coolant through the core. The coolant may be a gas or it may be a liquid, such as water, or even a molten metal, such as liquid sodium. Once removed from the reactor core, the heat is transferred in a heat exchanger to convert water into steam and turn a turbine. In other words, the heart of a nuclear reactor substitutes for the firebox of a conventional coal-steam-electric plant. Thus uranium may be looked upon as a substitute for coal.

One pound of uranium can produce the heat or power of 2,300,000 pounds of coal. However, there has to be enough uranium in a nuclear reactor to bring it up to criticality—that is, to a point where more neutrons are produced than are lost in or from the system. In the case of the first Chicago reactor, it took about seven tons of uranium to achieve criticality. This was what we call ordinary or normal uranium, meaning with its normal composition of 99.3 per cent U^{238} and 0.7 per cent U^{235}. The original pile, therefore, contained about one hundred pounds of U^{235}. However, the graphite and the uranium used were not so pure as can be obtained today. Therefore, we can assume that if one could produce pure U^{235}, considerably less than one hundred pounds would suffice to achieve a critical mass.

How does one go about getting pure U^{235}? A rather naïve but straightforward answer is: separate it from the more abundant U^{238}. The recipe here is simply stated but exceedingly difficult to follow, since the light and heavy isotopes of uranium are intimately mixed together and both behave the same chemically. Therefore, any method devised to separate the cousins must be a physical rather than a chemical method. We saw earlier that it was possible to separate these isotopes with a mass spectrograph, so this is one possibility. However, since uranium is also available in gaseous form in a compound called uranium hexafluoride or UF_6, a method that turned out to work better is known as the gaseous diffusion process. The principle involved here is similar to that of a sieve. Large pebbles can be separated from finer ones by shaking the mixture over a grating or screen. In the case of uranium we apply this principle to gas molecules, on the theory that the molecules containing the light isotopes of uranium will move a trifle faster than those containing the heavier, sluggish atoms. Scientists thought that if they pumped the uranium gas up against a very fine sieve, the faster moving, U^{235}-containing molecules would pass through the porous barrier somewhat more readily than those containing the U^{238} atoms. Naturally the holes in the sieve had to be ultramicroscopic in size; otherwise the gas would stream through the sieve with no preference for the lighter, faster U^{235} molecules.

During the war a tremendous effort was focused on designing and then building a huge gaseous diffusion plant at Oak Ridge, Tennessee. The illustration may give some idea of the magnitude of the task, especially when one realizes that this plant was built at a cost of $550 million. This separation

27. An aerial view of the enormous uranium separation plant at Oak Ridge, Tennessee. The final product of this huge plant is enriched uranium which costs about $7,000 per pound. (Atomic Energy Commission)

plant, like the ones built after the war near Paducah, Kentucky, and Portsmouth, Ohio, contains almost 300,000 miles of stainless steel pipe through which the uranium gas is processed. This is more than enough pipe to stretch from the earth to the moon. As the uranium gas diffuses or filters through one sieve or porous plug, it collects on the other side, slightly greater in its U^{235} content. We say that it is enriched in its U^{235} percentage. By recycling this slightly enriched gas through several thousand stages the uranium-235 content is boosted until it emerges about 95 per cent U^{235} and 5 per cent U^{238}.

Stripping the U^{235} from natural uranium requires a large input of uranium to produce the desired end product. Allowing for some losses in the process, it is reasonable to assume that it takes about a ton of normal uranium to produce about ten pounds of enriched material of the 95 per cent variety. Even under the most modern conditions the cost of production runs somewhere between $7,000 and $8,000 per pound. A vast amount of electrical energy is required to operate these plants; today, in fact, atomic production facilities in the U.S.A. consume over 10 per cent of the nation's electricity. The uranium feed material for U.S. atomic plants costs roughly $500 million per year.

Such huge expenditures for uranium greatly stimulated the search for new uranium deposits. No one really expected to find a new Shinkolobwe mine, but it was hoped that low-grade ore beds would be discovered.

An extensive exploration program in the United States revealed that huge beds of uranium ore were located in New Mexico—in the Ambrosia Lake fields, where thick deposits occur three hundred to a thousand feet below the earth's surface. This ore assays from 0.1 to 0.5 per cent uranium but it is estimated that the New Mexico deposits include up to thirty million tons of ore. Uranium deposits in Colorado, Arizona, Wyoming and a few Western states probably contain about the same amount of similar ore.

Canada has long been a source of uranium and after the war new finds were made and a greatly accelerated program of ore exploitation was undertaken. As a result, experts now estimate the ultimate Canadian reserve as one-quarter billion tons of uranium and they readily admit that much of Canada's northland has yet to be explored.

Africa continues to provide high-grade uranium ore, but

from deepening seams, which increases the cost of production. However, a new source of African uranium ore was discovered in the waste products of the South African gold and diamond mines. Veritable mountains of discarded ore residues or tailings had accumulated outside the gold refineries. These worthless residues were found to contain several times more uranium than they had contained gold. Even though the percentage of uranium is small, these sources now outrank the Belgian Congo as uranium producers.

Elsewhere around the globe, especially in Australia, uranium finds were made as the hunt for the valuable metal of the Atomic Age quickened. Little is known of the uranium mining behind the Iron Curtain but it must be assumed that with such a vast land mass the Soviets must have adequate reserves of uranium. It is now agreed that there is sufficient uranium to provide atomic fuel to outlast coal and oil twenty-five times over.

These discoveries were still in the future, however, when—long before U^{235} was available in any quantity—a small task force of scientists, under the leadership of young Dr. J. Robert Oppenheimer, set out to explore the means by which explosive energy might be wrested from the uranium atom. One of the most ticklish problems that the scientists gathered at Los Alamos had to solve was to determine how much bomb material would be required to make a bomb. Unlike TNT, which can be stacked sky-high without danger of self-explosion, the tricky bomb stuff is most unusual. If you take a very small piece of bomb stuff you can do almost anything to it—hammer it, heat it, or whatever you wish. Nothing will happen. But the moment you assemble too much in one place, it will chain-react and start to explode.

Let's see what takes place inside an assembly of the critical bomb stuff. If we start out with a small amount of material, say about the size of a golf ball, no chain reaction occurs. This is because the neutrons produced in fission travel a considerable distance—about an inch—between collisions. This means that in a small sphere the size of a golf ball most of the neutrons would escape and be lost to space.

Where do the neutrons come from in the first place? As we have noted earlier, they may come from a number of sources. Cosmic rays bombarding the earth produce a small number of neutrons, and spontaneous fission occurring in a few uranium atoms may provide the neutrons to start a chain reaction. But to speed up the process, scientists use an artificial source of neutrons—radium-beryllium—in their experiments.

Suppose we contrive to enlarge the size of our uranium golf ball, making it a little larger step by step? The larger the sphere becomes, the less chance the neutrons have of flying out into space. More and more the fission neutrons will be trapped within the confines of the uranium; these will cause more fission and, of course, produce more neutrons. In this way the number of neutrons will tend to build up. At a certain critical point the loss of neutrons through the surface of the sphere will be offset by the greater productions of neutrons inside. We then have a critical mass of material, and the chain reaction is ready to rip the moment that more material is added.

Experiments had to be performed at the Los Alamos Laboratory to determine just how much was critical. We called it "tickling the dragon's tail" for it was a rather dangerous experiment. Here is the way that it was conducted by young Dr. Louis Slotin. He would take two pieces of bomb stuff, each less than the critical amount, usually hemispheres which together would be the size of a baseball. The trick in the experiment was to bring the hemispheres slowly together and to measure the build-up of neutrons with a counter. Slotin arranged this by having a neutron counter record the build-up audibly, so that he could in effect listen to the pulse of the incipient chain reaction. He also fed part of the counter's signal into a pen and ink recorder which traced a red line on a sheet of graph paper. Thus at a glance, Slotin could note how fast the curve of neutron intensity was going up.

Slotin would then put his two pieces of bomb stuff on a horizontal rack on a table. Then he would push them slowly toward each other, carefully noting the rate at which the neutrons were multiplying. He grew very adept at judging the critical point and would stop the experiment when the hemispheres were still separated. By measuring the degree of separation he could calculate how much the critical mass would be.

Even the most careful experimenter can make mistakes. In this instance a mistake could be fatal. One day, and ironically it was to be the last time Slotin had to do the task, he had an accident. He was demonstrating to six other members of the scientific staff how to do the experiment. They stood behind him as he repeated his delicate operation of tickling the dragon's tail. But it was once too often. Somehow, he slipped and the two hemispheres went together in a supercritical assembly. The counters screamed a furious whine as the neutrons raced loose in an uncontrolled chain reaction. On the graph paper the red ink line swept off scale. But the young scientist moved with all the speed of reflex action. He had no thought for his personal safety—he knew all too well that he had a naked A-bomb core or "nuke" under his hands. He threw himself forward and tore the chain-reacting mass apart with his bare hands.

The chain reaction stopped. But the damage was done, for while there had not been an atomic explosion there had been a radiation explosion. Some heat came off from the assembly and Slotin, afterward, remarked that he felt a dry, acid-like taste in his mouth. But he felt nothing else, other than a chill of horror. A great burst of neutrons and gamma rays had flashed through his body. But his quick action had stopped the racing pulse of the reaction and his own body, hunched over the table, had shielded the others from most of the penetrating rays.

Nine days later, Slotin died a very unpleasant death, a victim of radiation sickness. He had received more than a lethal dose of radiation and there was nothing that anyone could do to help him, other than to ease his pain. The others in the room were hospitalized but they all recovered after a brief illness. Some were not even sickened by the effects of radiation.

Slotin's critical experiment has been outlawed and no one in our country is endangered by repetition of similar experiments which are conducted by the Los Alamos Laboratory. The modern technique uses remote control equipment and television cameras. All assemblies are made in a concrete revetment which is a quarter-mile from the control center.

Making a real atomic explosion involves the same principles we have already discussed in the Slotin experiment. But instead of making the assembly of the bomb stuff slowly, it has to be done very fast. Otherwise, the assembly would simply heat up and expand until it was no longer critical. The trick in making an A-bomb is to slam the subcritical pieces of bomb stuff together as fast as possible and to keep them together long enough for the chain reaction to fission a significant number of the atoms.

There are two general methods for making such a rapid-fire assembly of bomb parts. One method involves two pieces of bomb material, which are placed at either end of a closed gun barrel. This device is known as the Gun. At the target end there is a subcritical amount of bomb material imbedded in a massive tamper of heavy metal. In the gun barrel is a projectile of the same material backed by a propellant. The propellant is detonated by means of a fuse and fires the projectile at the target.

As the projectile fuses into the target, it lets loose the

28. Jezebel is the name given to this remote-controlled critical assembly device installed at Los Alamos, New Mexico. A sphere about the size of a softball is brought together from the three components and criticality is controlled by the flat bar which moves in and out of the central piece of fissionable material. (Los Alamos Scientific Laboratory)

chain reaction. In one-millionth of one second the chain reaction races to completion and what was previously a cool glistening metal is transformed into a raging hot gas. It blossoms forth to become a multimillion-degree explosion. This is what happened early on the morning of July 16, 1945, when scientists gathered together at Alamogordo to witness the first test of an A-bomb. It is also what happened over Japan when bombs were dropped over Hiroshima and Nagasaki.

The bomb dropped on Hiroshima was the Gun type. But the bombs tested at Alamogordo and over Nagasaki were different and more sophisticated weapons. They operated on a different principle, which permitted a more complete chain reaction and thus used up more of the fissionable material. They were, in other words, more efficient, and depended upon a new principle of assembly called *implosion*.

To describe the implosion-type weapon we start at the very center, which we shall call the "nuke." It is composed of a hollow sphere of bomb stuff, either U^{235} or plutonium (which, as we shall see later, fissions as easily as U^{235}). Inside the baseball-sized sphere is a hollow ping-pong ball-like object which is a polonium-beryllium source of neutrons. The beryllium is insulated from the alpha rays of polonium by a mere plating of metal. Outside the "nuke" is a heavy tamper of dense metal; outside this is a thick mantle of high-explosive material. This outer jacket of TNT is in the form of many prisms of high explosive which are fitted together so as to form a solid overcoat around the inner nuke and its tamper. Each prism of high explosive is connected to a detonator which can explode it upon receipt of an electrical impulse. A special electronic circuit is wrapped around the bulky sphere to feed this impulse to all prisms at exactly the same time.

Detonating this A-bomb explodes the outer TNT mantle and, as one would naturally expect, produces a big explosion, since some thousands of pounds of TNT are involved. Everyone knows that this produces considerable blast. But in this case there is also an inwardly direct blast wave or implosion. This gigantic inward blast punch collapses the inner nuke into an overcritical assembly and the chain reaction starts. It happens that this method of assembly is very effective and burns up more of the fissionable material than the Gun-type weapon.

These, then, were the weapons of 1945. Rated in terms of their blast power they were the equal of about 20,000 tons of TNT. They were sufficient to tear the heart out of a great city like Hiroshima. But they were only primitive low-power weapons compared to the giants of today, the thousandfold more powerful super bombs, often called H-bombs in the popular press.

11=

The Controlled Atom

THE control of the nuclear chain reaction actually preceded the detonation of the A-bomb. This was necessary because nuclear chain reactions were required to produce a bomb material as a substitute for uranium-235 should the latter have been impossible to produce in quantity. The substitute bomb stuff is an element that man created by bombarding ordinary uranium with neutrons. In the next chapter we describe the discovery of new elements; here we shall simply assume that uranium, element 92, can be transformed into plutonium, element 94.

Fermi's purpose in designing chain-reacting machines was to produce a nuclear reactor that would generate vast numbers of neutrons. These, in turn, would be swallowed up by uranium-238 and convert it into plutonium. Using the experience gained with the chain-reacting units built at Chicago and later at Oak Ridge, Tennessee, scientists designed new, more powerful machines, which were set up on the banks of the Columbia River in a rather desolate part of the state of Washington.

The sole purpose of these nuclear reactors was the production of plutonium. They were designed so that the uranium that was bombarded by neutrons inside the reactor core could be taken out and chemically processed to remove the plutonium. This presented a great challenge to scientists and engineers, because the uranium would also contain split atoms or fission fragments. The intense radioactivity of these split atoms made it necessary to take elaborate precautions so that no one would be exposed to harmful radiation. The core of the machine was essentially a huge cube of carbon or graphite blocks which were so arranged that long tubes of aluminum passed from one side of the cube to the other. Many hundreds of heavy uranium cylinders (called "slugs") were pushed into the aluminum channels. Each uranium slug was carefully jacketed with a can of aluminum sealed so that no split atoms would be released.

Eventually a reactor was so designed that every ten atoms of uranium, when split, released enough neutrons to produce eight atoms of plutonium, converted from uranium-238. As there are twelve million, million, billion atoms of plutonium in a pound, it required seventeen billion, billion atoms of uranium-235 splitting every second to produce one pound of plutonium in one day. We have already seen that when the uranium splits, the fragments fly apart with very high speed—far greater than the speed of the man-made satellites which whiz around the earth. The immense energy locked inside the atom is partially released to the flying fragments; these smash into other atoms and are quickly robbed of their energy. The atomic energy thus released appears in the form of heat.

Although the amount of heat produced by the splitting of a single atom is small, when we deal with billions upon billions of atom-splittings every second, the resulting heat is exceedingly intense. The temperature inside the huge reactors at Hanford, Washington, would quickly rise and the uranium would melt, spewing out dangerous radioactivity, and the entire structure would be destroyed, unless the device were cooled. In order to keep the reactor from melting down, the cool water from the Columbia River is pumped through the aluminum channels, thus transferring the heat from the uranium slugs to the water. This heated water is allowed to cool briefly after discharge from the plant, and then it flows back into the Columbia River.

Enough heat was produced in these war-built atomic reactors to provide energy for a large city. However, since the sole purpose of the machines was to produce plutonium, the heat was a waste product. To convert this heat into useful energy, preferably in the form of cheap electricity, is an engineering task that has not been fully accomplished even today. In principle, it was obvious that the uranium atom was a potent source of energy; this was quite clear from the momentous events that took place at Hiroshima and Nagasaki. However, taming this atomic energy was destined to be an engineering assignment of staggering magnitude.

One of the very first uses that was suggested for harnessed atomic power was in submarine propulsion. In fact, in March of 1939, Enrico Fermi approached the U.S. Navy Department to sell the Navy on this idea. Nothing much came of the proposal, partly because the War Department took on the task of wartime atomic development and partly because the wartime aim was the A-bomb rather than a new source of propulsion. Shortly after the war, a most unusual naval officer fixed his sights on the goal of an atomic submarine.

Admiral (then Captain) H. G. Rickover threw himself into this project with all his dynamic energy. His enthusiasm for his work contrasted with the apathetic attitude of the U.S. Navy, but Rickover drove ahead relentlessly. Uranium appealed to him as an ideal fuel for underwater propulsion. A single pound of the new fuel was the equal of a quarter-million gallons of fuel oil. Unlike the internal combustion engine, a nuclear machine required no air. Thus, if such a machine could be made in practical form, an atomic submarine could make prolonged, high-speed, submerged cruises.

The hard-bitten naval officer knew that the revolutionary new power plant for the first atomic submarine would be a tough job. He did not need anything as powerful as the reactors on the banks of the Columbia River, but even a machine one-tenth as powerful would still be too big to fit inside a submarine hull. A new design had to be made. Rickover assigned part of the task to the Westinghouse Electrical and Manufacturing Company.

The heart of the problem was to design a reactor core small enough to be practical for a submarine and powerful enough to propel the craft at superior speed. The design

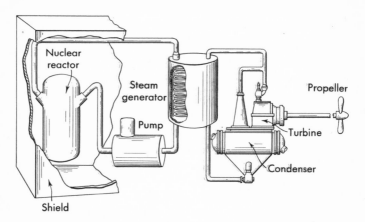

29. Schematic view of the nuclear engine for the U.S.S. Nautilus. (Westinghouse Electric Corp.)

adopted consisted of a cylindrical vessel inside which were many slender rods of valuable uranium-235. Circulating around these fuel rods was purified water, pumped under pressure. A series of metal pipes running lengthwise through the cylindrical chamber served to "pipe out the heat" from the reactor core; water in these tubes took up the heat and passed into a heat transfer system.

Here we may interrupt the description of a nuclear power plant by pointing out that once heat is produced in any power plant, whether from uranium or from the combustion of coal or oil, the heat is used in a conventional manner. Engineers handle steam at high pressure and at high temperature all the time in the coal-steam plants which produce electricity in our cities. In a nuclear power plant, the steam is shot into a turbine, hitting the blades and thus turning the shaft. A generator attached to the shaft produces electrical power.

Why was this engineering task so difficult in the case of a submarine reactor? There were many technical problems to be solved in developing materials that would stand up under the high temperatures and radiations inside the reactor core. Furthermore, most construction materials used in conventional boilers contain elements that are unsuitable for nuclear reactors. However, the most troublesome aspect of nuclear engineering is the need to shield against the penetrating radiation emitted in the reactor core. The huge reactors that produce plutonium are surrounded on all sides by concrete shields many feet thick. These blankets absorb the harmful rays and allow people to work near the reactor without suffering any injury. But shielding a submarine reactor is a tricky business, because the weight and volume of shielding material must be kept small enough to fit inside the hull.

The first U.S. atom-propelled submarine was named the *Nautilus* after the legendary craft that Jules Verne described in his *Twenty Thousand Leagues Under the Sea*. In order to make sure that the first prototype engine would simulate actual submarine conditions, it was built into two hull sections at the Arco, Idaho, site of the Atomic Energy Commission. At this desert location, a "sea tank" holding about 400,000 gallons of water was built to surround the hull. This first experimental atomic engine in its test hull is shown in the accompanying photograph.

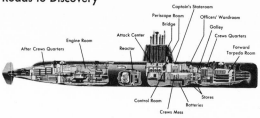

30. The U.S.S. *Nautilus*, a cutaway view showing inner details of the world's first atomic submarine. (U.S. Navy)

On January 21, 1954, the U.S.S. *Nautilus* slid down its ways at Groton, Connecticut, and not too long after that the twin, five-bladed propellers were churning up a wake in the Thames River. The world's first A-powered submarine was a reality. The plump undersea craft soon established speed and endurance records far outdistancing the performances of conventional subs. The *Nautilus* cruised 62,500 miles without refueling; the same performance would have burned up over two million gallons of fuel oil in an ordinary submarine. The U.S. Navy, previously skeptical about atom-powered ships, saw in the *Nautilus* the beginning of a nuclear-powered fleet. As a result, new and improved types of nuclear craft were authorized. In 1958 the U.S.S. *Skate* put to sea to join its pioneer sister. Both atomic subs created newspaper headlines when they traveled under the ice packs at the North Pole.

Other atomic submarines bearing such fishy names as *Skipjack, Triton, Halibut, Swordfish* and *Seadragon* will join the *Nautilus*. By 1961 the U.S. Navy will have a small, but highly effective, fleet of modern submarines. The *Triton* is the largest submarine ever constructed, displacing some eight thousand tons and costing more than $100 million. The newest models of these undersea craft will be high-speed designs equipped to fire Polaris ballistic missiles from under the surface of the sea. High military priority is being given to this new weapons system.

A nuclear cruiser, the U.S.S. *Long Beach*, will displace

fourteen thousand tons and will serve as a mobile base for launching guided missiles. Powered by twin reactors, the cruiser is expected to have a speed in excess of forty knots.

The U.S. Navy's biggest nuclear venture is the *Enterprise*, an 86,000-ton supercarrier with a flight deck 1,100 feet long. The length of this flight deck is almost four times the length of a football field. A total of eight nuclear reactors will provide the propulsive thrust to push this supercarrier through the waves at speeds of thirty-three knots.

In the early 1960s the U.S. Navy will be a big user of uranium power. It will have atomic power plants at sea which will add up to more than one million kilowatts of power capacity. It is understandable that the Navy should be the first large-scale user of uranium power once we consider that the armed services do not count costs in the same way that a municipal government must when planning a new electric power plant. A city's leaders would be roundly criticized if they elected to install a nuclear-electric plant that was more expensive to build and to operate than those now in use. Citizens would be irate when their monthly electric bills went up. Thus the choice of nuclear versus conventional power plants is largely a matter of dollars and cents. This serves to explain why there are so few large nuclear power plants now operating in the United States; the costs to date have proven to be too high.

While it is an impressive fact that one pound of uranium is the power equivalent of 2,300,000 pounds of coal, this figure does not take into account the additional costs that are necessary to construct a nuclear power plant. The need to protect against radiation hazards raises the cost of nuclear power stations. The new technology of special materials necessary for designing reactors also contributes to higher costs. Then, too, the uranium fuel cannot be completely "burned" in the reactor, but must be removed when only a small fraction of it has been consumed. This is because the burn-up of nuclear fuel in the fuel rod produces drastic changes in the physical properties of the structure and the fuel elements would be severely damaged if they were left too long inside a reactor. This means that the rods must be periodically discharged from the reactor and chemically reprocessed in order to reclaim the nuclear fuel that has not been burned. Such reprocessing is very costly and adds to the over-all expense of the nuclear power plant.

When an ordinary steam electric plant blows up, the explosion of the boiler usually causes damage only over a short distance; often only within the plant site. The same would probably be true of nuclear power plants so far as the blast effect is concerned. However, the big worry is that the fuel elements might rupture and spew their radioactive contents into the air. Such an accident close to a populated area could be a major disaster. Some of the nuclear power plants built in the U.S. have attempted to solve this problem by enclosing the entire reactor within a spherical pressure shell, which would contain the debris in the event of a reactor accident. This additional construction also considerably increases the plants' costs.

Nonetheless, a small number of large nuclear power stations have been built. The first U.S. plant of this type was built at Shippingport, Pennsylvania, not far from Pittsburgh. It was put up in order to provide practical engineering and operating experience, even though it was known in advance that the power costs would not come close to competing with the cheap coal in the vicinity of Pittsburgh. The Shippingport plant cost a total of $110 million and was designed to produce 60,000 kilowatts of electricity to begin with; it is hoped to raise this level to 100,000 kilowatts in the future. The Shippingport plant operates along much the same lines as the *Nautilus* engine, although it is of course much more powerful and much more massive. The over-all cost of this nuclear electricity is roughly ten times that of coal-produced electrical

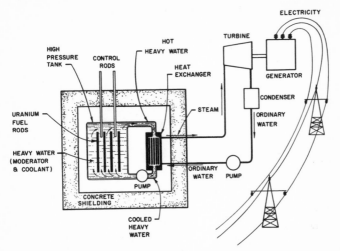

ELECTRICITY

TURBINE

HOT
HEAVY WATER

HIGH
PRESSURE
TANK

CONTROL
RODS

HEAT
EXCHANGER

GENERATOR

CONDENSER

STEAM

ORDINARY
WATER

URANIUM
FUEL
RODS

HEAVY WATER
(MODERATOR
& COOLANT)

ORDINARY
WATER   PUMP

PUMP

CONCRETE
SHIELDING

COOLED
HEAVY
WATER

31. A heavy-water-cooled nuclear power plant for generating electricity.

energy, but improvements in the fuel elements may cut the figure sharply. However, there is little possibility of bringing the costs down to a point where this plant will compete with a modern coal-steam plant.

A number of nuclear power plants have advanced designs which permit their electrical output to be considerably lower in cost than that from the Shippingport station. One such plant has been built at Dresden, Illinois, not far from Chicago; it is scheduled for full-scale operation in 1960. Total power production from the Commonwealth Edison plant at Dresden is rated as 180,000 kilowatts.

A 134,000-kilowatt nuclear power plant has been constructed by the Yankee Electric Company at Rowe, Massachusetts, and is expected to be in full operation in 1961. The Consolidated Edison Company expects its giant 255,000-kilowatt plant north of New York City to operate in the same year.

Not far from Detroit, near Lagoona Beach, a novel nuclear

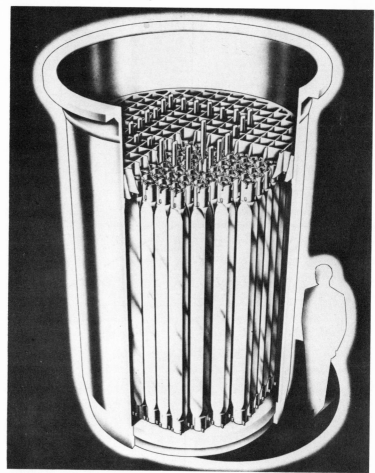

32. The core of the first U.S. atomic-electric plant. The uranium fuel rods are sealed in zirconium alloy jackets and positioned inside the reactor vessel. Water flows under pressure up through the rods and carries the heat to external heat exchangers. (Westinghouse Electric Co., Atomic Power Division)

power plant is being constructed. Known as the Enrico Fermi plant, it is a power-breeder designed to produce 90,000 kilowatts of electricity and to "breed" more new nuclear fuel than it consumes. The reactor core is relatively small and consists of a cluster of fuel rods immersed in liquid sodium. Outside the core is a blanket of uranium-238. Neutrons flashing out into the uranium blanket are absorbed and plutonium is produced by the nuclear capture. The reactor is so designed that it will burn up about 200 pounds of uranium-235 inside the core and at the same time generate about 240 pounds of plutonium outside the core, for a net gain of 40 pounds of nuclear fuel.

All of this has a slightly unreal aspect, since it appears that one is getting something for nothing. In fact, if one could sell the excess plutonium to the government for about $1,000 an ounce while paying much less than that for the uranium-235 fuel, it would sound like a get-rich-quick scheme. Actually, one is not creating nuclear fuel from some worthless element. One is converting uranium into plutonium and thus extending the world's uranium resources. With breeding it is theoretically possible to tap all of the uranium supply, both the energy from uranium-235 and that from uranium-238. Were it not possible to convert uranium-238 into a nuclear fuel, then only 0.7 per cent of the uranium—the uranium-235 content—could be tapped for energy. By a similar process, thorium can be converted into a useful nuclear fuel; thus man has at his disposal the resources of both uranium and thorium.

The world's resources of nuclear fuel in the earth's crust are truly enormous. There are roughly ten million tons of this precious material which can be exploited—the equivalent of 20,000 billion tons of coal. Man is using up his fossil fuels (coal, oil and natural gas) at an ever-increasing rate in order to satisfy the demands of an expanding population and a dynamic industrial economy. At one time reserves of coal and oil seemed more than adequate for man's needs. But the world today burns up five hundred times more fuel than it did a century ago, and soon this consumption will double, triple and climb upward. Petroleum reserves are known to be limited, and one does not have to look beyond the end of this century to forecast a deficit in our production-consumption balance of liquid fuels.

Nuclear power as an industry has had a slow start but once its advantages are demonstrated, a brisk pace is assured for the growth of this new power source. Experts predict that by the end of this century the uranium atom will have replaced coal as the preferred fuel for new power plants. They foresee by then a tremendous nuclear power industry with a capacity of 500 million kilowatts of installed capacity.

Unlike conventional power plants, in which the ashes and clinkers are a minor nuisance, nuclear plants involve a great hazard in the disposal of their radioactive ashes or wastes. For example, a typical large power plant produces radioactive ashes equal to many tons of radium as far as radiation hazard is concerned. We have already mentioned that only a fraction of the nuclear fuel can be burned up in the fuel rods; this means that unused fuel and radioactive ashes are intimately mixed together. Chemical processing is required to separate the two; this requires very large quantities of chemical solutions, which become highly radioactive. It is estimated that by the end of the century about two billion gallons of radioactive waste will have accumulated. A safe and permanent method of waste disposal must be found, and it appears that some type of storage in the earth's crust is the solution. Salt mines have been suggested as the best-suited geological formations to hold the wastes and prevent escape of the radiation to the air or to ground water.

Nuclear power as a means of naval propulsion and as a producer of electricity loom as the two largest uses for this new energy source in the 1960s. It is possible that the Navy's experience may pave the way for the addition of nuclear-powered ships to our merchant fleet, but costs for such power plants are presently so high that nonmilitary nuclear shipping is quite far in the future. In order to approach being economic, nuclear power plants have to have a very large capacity; thus ship reactors of relatively medium power are not economic. Furthermore, the limited space for shipboard installation forces changes in the design of reactors, which also raises costs.

Barring some radical innovation in reactor design, there is little prospect that nuclear engines will be used for very low power sources such as in automobiles, trucks and buses. Atomic locomotives are technically possible but not very attractive, since costs would be high and the hazards of a train wreck would be potentially disastrous. It is far more likely that trains will be indirectly powered by the atom; that is, electric trains will run on lines fed with electricity generated by large, stationary nuclear power plants.

The possibility of atomic-powered flight has been in the headlines for over fifteen years. Some highly futuristic reporting has led people to believe that an atomic aircraft has been perfected and is ready for flight testing. In fact, the U.S. Air Force has been working on its ANP (Aircraft, Nuclear Propulsion) project intensively for many years; by 1960 it will have spent close to one billion dollars on a nuclear bomber. There is little doubt that a huge aircraft can be made to fly on A-power; but there is considerable question about the military capabilities of such a bomber.

In principle, the A-plane is a massive, jet-propelled device in which heat from uranium-fueled reactors substitutes for the energy provided by burning jet fuel. The intense heat from powerful nuclear reactors is transferred to the air stream sucked into the nuclear jet engine. Because of the intense radioactivity and the difficulty of providing sufficient shielding (the weight is prohibitive), the crew is stationed at the tip of the bomber. This design minimizes the amount of radiation to which the crew is exposed.

It is still too soon to evaluate the future potential of nuclear-powered bombers, but there is general agreement that

A-powered aircraft for civilian use will be sky-high in price and out of reach of commercial operations. As in the case of nuclear submarines, the armed services put military worth ahead of dollars and cents.

The dawning of the Space Age has focused attention upon fuels capable of blasting rockets to higher speeds with greater and greater payloads. Naturally, scientists have looked to uranium as a superior fuel for rocket use. Conventional rockets, using chemical fuels, function by burning an energy-rich hydrocarbon fuel in the presence of pure oxygen. The oxygen has to be carried along in the rocket in the form of liquid oxygen or LOX. When the explosive mixture is ignited in the rocket's combustion chamber, there is a fearful roar and hot gases are expelled rapidly through the nozzle at the end of the missile. This ejection of hot gas pushes the rocket off its launching pad and the missile hurtles into the sky. Contrary to popular belief, the missile does not rise heavenward by pushing against the atmosphere. In fact, it propels itself more efficiently in empty space, where there is no air resistance. If there were no atmosphere on our planet a rocket would take off more quickly.

Rocket propulsion is essentially a matter of action and reaction. If a man acts by diving headlong from the stern of a rowboat, the boat reacts by moving ahead. If one accomplishes the feat of diving from a canoe, the light boat spurts ahead, because it is much lighter than a rowboat. In the same way, a rocket moves forward by the rearward expulsion of hot gas. The lighter and hotter (higher speed) the gas, the better will be the efficiency of propulsion.

A nuclear rocket is still a rocket and must obey the same laws of propulsion. The nuclear part of the rocket engine is a reactor which produces heat—equivalent to the combustion of chemical fuels in the nonatomic rocket. However, all this great outpouring of heat would be useless for rocket propulsion; to be effective, a light gas must be heated up and expelled through the rocket engine nozzle. This is precisely the way that atomic engineers are going about the job in a U.S. defense effort known as Project Rover.

Project Rover aims at developing a nuclear rocket engine which is a compact, high-power, nuclear reactor. Engineers plan to pump liquid hydrogen through the glowing reactor core and convert the supercold liquid into a blazing hot gas. As in an ordinary rocket, the hot gas propels the missile skyward. Project Rover is out of the "dream stage" but is still in its technological infancy. Scientists and engineers have yet to solve the problem of developing materials that will stand up to the extreme conditions necessary for the rocket engine. However, they are confident that a nuclear rocket is attainable. They are encouraged in their efforts by the promise of a superior rocket fuel—uranium. The exploration of space, especially the outer space far beyond our planet, will be made possible through the control of the atom.

12-

The Family of Atoms

OUR earth, the other planets, our sun and the most distant stars constitute the visible universe. It is a celestial collection of glittering complexity and staggering magnitude. The huge 200-inch telescope at Mount Palomar looks out through a vastness of space and identifies light sources so far away that it takes two billion years for the light to reach the earth. Since light travels through space at the speed of 186,000 miles per second, this means that the edge of the universe is over ten thousand, billion, billion miles away!

Through the sensitivity of the ingenious instruments that man has fashioned, the depths of space have been probed. The faint flickerings of light from the farthest stars suffice to throw illumination on their elemental composition. Man is limited in his observation of the stars by the obscuring haze of the earth's atmosphere. This limitation will be conquered when rockets take instruments, and eventually man, to satellite or lunar observatories. But even with the data now available scientists have made great headway in solving the cosmic puzzle.

Nuclear physicists have joined with astronomers in seeking

keys to the puzzle. The approach of the atomic scientist has been to apply knowledge gained from laboratory experiments with atoms to theories that may explain the nature of stars and perhaps of the universe.

Analysis of the light emitted by stars allows scientists to determine their composition, because the atoms of each element emit characteristic wave lengths of light which uniquely identify them. For example, hydrogen is easily identified in light emitted by our sun. So, too, is iron and many other elements, including helium, which was first discovered in the sun—even before it was found on earth.

All the billions of stars in the universe are composed of known elements that have been found on earth. They may exist at very high temperatures and at very great pressures deep inside brilliantly shining stars but nonetheless they are the very same elements. By far the most abundant element in the universe is hydrogen—the simplest and lightest of all the atoms. This fact suggests that perhaps hydrogen is a fundamental building block of all stellar structures. Under the unusual conditions prevailing inside stars, elemental hydrogen may be fused together to form heavier elements such as helium; beyond helium, we may postulate the building up of even more complex atoms and thus account for the origin of all elements. This is the exciting path along which some scientists are questing today.

To come down to earth and to look at what is beneath our feet and easily within reach, let us consider the family of atoms that we have at home. Chemists have been busy at the task of sorting out the elements ever since the earliest scientists divided things into fire, earth, air and water. Through the patient efforts of legions of scientists in many lands, all substances, minerals, liquids, gases and organic matter were analyzed. Certain elements formed chemical compounds in similar ways and gradually it was realized that there was a regular or systematic arrangement of the elements, beginning with hydrogen and ending with uranium. As we have already explained, the elements could be numbered, starting with atomic number 1 for hydrogen and extending up to 92 for uranium. To be sure, there was a gap here and there in the Periodic Arrangement of the Elements, but it was reasoned that these belonged to "missing elements," which would be discovered in the future—as, indeed, they were.

Not all the atoms of a given element were the same in weight, although the atoms of some, such as gold, tantalum, beryllium and phosphorus, were found to be unvarying in weight. But copper and silver and, in fact, the majority of the elements were composed of atoms of different weight, or isotopes, to use the correct term. All in all, the gamut of elements from the lightest (hydrogen-1) to the heaviest (uranium-238) included a total of close to 300 isotopes or nuclear species.

Elements have very distinct preferences for the way in which they build up out of the fundamental structural units —neutrons and protons. The atom of a light element such as aluminum has a total of 27 neutrons and protons in its core or nucleus—13 protons and 14 neutrons. As one goes up the Periodic Scale to a middle-weight element like iodine (atomic number 53) one finds 74 neutrons and 53 protons in the iodine-127 nucleus. The predominance of neutrons becomes even more exaggerated in the heavy-weight uranium-238 nucleus, where there are 146 neutrons and 92 protons. For any given number of protons there are only certain combinations with neutrons that produce stable nuclei. Iodine-127 has only one such combination; if one forces the nucleus to hold more than 74 neutrons, it rebels, becomes unstable or radioactive, and undergoes a transformation by emitting a beta ray, thus changing itself into an atom of xenon.

We know from our discussion of radioactivity that some of the heavy elements are naturally unstable. There are four naturally radioactive series which descend from the heaviest atoms such as uranium-238. Radium-226 is a member of one of these series; it has a half-life of 1,600 years, which is short-lived compared with the age of the earth. We find radium in nature because it is being continually formed by the disintegration of long-lived uranium. Uranium-238, for example, has a half-life of 4.5 billion years. Since the earth was formed some five billion years ago, a little more than half of the uranium-238 has disappeared. In its place today we have lead-206, which is the tail end of the uranium series. Uranium-containing minerals, especially those from deposits that have been geologically undisturbed throughout time, may be used to measure the age of the earth. Measurement of the relative amounts of uranium-238 and lead-206 allows scientists to estimate directly when the mineral was formed. Such measurements have also been made on meteorites which have hit the earth. These atomic time-clock measurements give us confidence in the estimate that our solar system is roughly five billion years old.

In addition to the heavy radioactive elements, there are a few naturally occurring light atoms that are radioactive. These occur singly and are not a part of any radioactive series. One of the most important of these lone-wolf radioactive atoms is potassium-40. The average adult contains about one-half pound of potassium, and in this half pound there is about one-thousandth of an ounce of potassium-40. As a result of this potassium content, the average person is very slightly radioactive; he or she has about 7,000 disintegrations of potassium-40 taking place every second. This radiation contributes about one-fifth of the radiation dose that humans get from the natural background. Potassium-40 is a kind of freak atom, sticking out like a sore thumb among the other light elements. They too probably had many radioactive species when the earth was formed, but all except potassium-40 have vanished during the planet's history.

There is one other radioactive species among the light elements, namely carbon-14, but it has such a short half-life (5,700 years) that we must assume it is being constantly regenerated; otherwise it would all have disappeared. Carbon-14 is formed in the earth's atmosphere by the impact of cosmic ray neutrons upon nitrogen. The ensuing nuclear reaction produces carbon-14 which, in the form of carbon dioxide, makes its way into all living matter. The radiation dose to the human body is much less than that due to potassium.

Carbon-14 is of very practical importance because it allows us to date objects of the past—say, a sun boat from an Egyptian tomb. Since carbon-14 is constantly being produced in the earth's atmosphere, the planks used to construct sun boats were cut from trees that must have contained a certain amount of it. Obviously, when the tree was cut down the intake of carbon dioxide ceased. Today these samples of wood contain less carbon-14 because of the radioactive decay which has occurred in the intervening thousands of years. Knowing the rate at which carbon-14 decays, we can accurately date the age of the sun boat by measuring the remaining concentration of carbon-14 in the wood. Dr. Willard F. Libby is the scientist who pioneered in this fascinating technique for dating the past; it has since been used by archaeologists throughout the world.

The amount of carbon-14 naturally present in living matter is so small that special techniques are necessary to measure it. However, relatively large amounts can be produced through the use of cyclotrons and other accelerators. This artificially manufactured carbon-14 is a powerful diagnostic tool for research in biology and medicine. For example, it may be incorporated in a drug that is to be administered to an experimental animal or to a human being, but in such small amounts that there is no danger from radioactivity. Then, by examining samples of blood or tissue, one can trace the path of the carbon-14 through the organism. Such experimentation not only yields fundamental data on the basic mechanisms of the body, but also helps toward an understanding of how medical treatment may be advanced. A radioactive material used in this way is known as a tracer.

There are many other radioactive tracers, among them isotopes of phosphorus, sodium, iron and gold. These all permit wider exploration of the basic functions of human cells, and are also used in a wide variety of research in other fields. Infinitesimal amounts of radioisotopes, costing only a few cents, may be used with good results, whereas even a fraction of an ounce of radioactive phosphorus in pure form would cost a billion dollars.

Radioisotopes are proving of great value to the farmer, because agricultural research with tracers is helping scientists to understand the growth cycles of plants, to find out what is the best nutriment for various crops and to learn more efficient methods of combating plant pests. Atomic research of the past decade is paying off for the farmer in terms of better crops and less cost.

Industrialists are also enjoying the benefits of atomic science. Engine wear and lubricant efficiency are quickly determined by the use of radioisotopes. All manner of friction studies are facilitated with this new technique. For example, a rubber tire may be impregnated with small amounts of a radioisotope and the road wear studied with Geiger counters. Manufacturers of clothes washers can study the operation of their machines with radioactive tracers. The efficiency of soaps and detergents can be appraised by deliberately contaminating the clothes with a radioactive material and then measuring the loss of radioactivity when the clothes are cleaned with various types of detergents.

Cigarette manufacturers routinely employ nuclear radiation in radioactive gauges which maintain a constant check on the amount of tobacco in the paper-covered tubes. This is done by bombarding the cigarette with a beam of rays from a radioactive source. As the rays penetrate the tube they are more or less absorbed depending upon the amount of tobacco inside; too little or too much tobacco shows up in a change in the radiation that is measured on the other side of the cigarette by automatic electronic devices. The whole process is completely automatic, works swiftly so that there is no interruption of the production line (imperfect cigarettes are automatically flicked off the conveyor belt), and does no harm to the product.

Radioactive thickness gauges are widely used in industry for the purpose of controlling the thickness of rolled sheets, whether of steel, aluminum, paper, plastic or linoleum. As with the cigarette gauge, the radiation is directed against the sheet from one side and the amount of radiation passing through the swiftly moving strip is measured on the other side. The electronic instruments are so adjusted that if the gauge detects a thinning or a thickening of the strip, it relays the information to the rolling machine and adjustments are made automatically so that the sheet is rolled to a uniform thickness.

Every element has at least one radioactive species that can be produced artificially. Hydrogen, for example, normally consists of H^1 and H^2 (deuterium or double-weight hydrogen); a triple-weight species known as H^3 or T^3 (tritium) can be manufactured by bombarding lithium-6 with neutrons. Most of the light elements have 3, 4 or 5 radioisotopes, the middleweights many more. Iodine, for example, has only one stable isotope—iodine-127—but it has radioactive species ranging from iodine-119 up to iodine-139, for a total of twenty radioisotopes. Roughly 700 radioisotopes have been discovered in the Periodic Table as far as element 81. Beyond this point and up to element 92 we find both the species that are members of the natural radioactive series and those which can be produced artificially; there are about 170 of these nuclear species.

For a long time uranium stood as the outpost atom at the

end of the Periodic Table. Uranium-238 was the heaviest atom known to man. In 1936 Hahn and Strassmann, then working with Lise Meitner, had concluded that a still heavier atom was produced when uranium-238 was bombarded with neutrons. Neutron capture by uranium-238 should produce uranium-239, and this in turn, they reasoned, should undergo a radioactive transformation by emitting a beta particle to form an isotope of element 93. They were able to measure a 23-minute activity for uranium-239 but they were unable chemically to identify the new nuclear species, element 93.

From U-238 to Plutonium 239

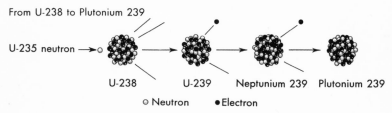

U-235 neutron →⊙

U-238   U-239   Neptunium 239   Plutonium 239

⊙ Neutron   ● Electron

33. Illustrating how a neutron capture in heavy uranium leads to the formation of a new element—plutonium.

Two American scientists were successful in discovering element 93 early in 1940. Drs. Edwin McMillan and Philip Abelson performed their experiments at the Radiation Laboratory of the University of California. They used a thin foil of uranium and bombarded it with neutrons. Naturally, this caused some of the uranium atoms to fission; the fission fragments thus produced were kicked out of the thin film, leaving behind a uranium sample uncontaminated with the highly radioactive fission fragments. This trick made it possible for McMillan and Abelson to study the uranium foil without being troubled by the interfering radioactivity of the fission fragments. They readily identified the 23-minute activity that Hahn and his colleagues had found and then went on to identify chemically the presence of a trace of element 93 which had remained in the foil.

They named the new element neptunium (Np) after the

planet Neptune, the closest neighbor of the planet Uranus. The particular species of neptunium discovered was Np^{239}, which the investigators were able to show decayed with a half-life of 2.3 days. Since an element jumps one place up in the Periodic Table when it emits a beta particle, the beta decay of Np^{239} should produce a species of element 94. McMillan and Abelson looked for evidence of this element but they were unable to find it.

In 1940, another group of California scientists, spearheaded by Dr. Glenn T. Seaborg, set out on a different trail to hunt for elements beyond uranium. They used a cyclotron to bombard uranium with a beam of heavy hydrogen ions (deuterons or H^2). The nuclear reaction that they produced is shown by the equation:

$$_{92}U^{238} \quad + \quad _1H^2 \quad = \quad _{93}Np^{238} \quad + \quad 2_0n^1$$
(uranium) (deuteron)   (neptunium)   (neutron)

This reaction may be described in terms of an in-out classification; one deuteron goes "in," meaning that it is swallowed up by uranium-238, and two neutrons fly "out." Since a deuteron consists of a single proton and a single neutron, this in-out reaction may be thought of as an exchange in which a proton changes place with a neutron inside the uranium nucleus. The mass number remains the same, but the interchange of a proton for a neutron is equivalent to jumping one place up in the Periodic Table, so the nuclear reaction must produce an isotope of neptunium, in this case, Np^{238}. Seaborg and his co-workers found that this isotope, in turn, decayed into a species of element 94, which they were able to identify chemically. This new element was christened plutonium (Pu) after the planet Pluto. The specific isotope identified was Pu^{238}; it was found to emit alpha particles, decaying with a half-life of ninety years. Later the isotope—Pu^{239}—that McMillan and Abelson had sought was identified and found to be an alpha-emitter with a half-life of 24,400 years.

Neptunium and plutonium are elements that man created in 1940. No doubt these new elements had once existed on earth, but because of their short lives they had long since vanished. These were exciting discoveries, for they meant that man had established a beachhead for the invasion of a whole new region lying beyond uranium in the Periodic System of Elements. Who could tell what other new elements might be found? Or what properties these man-made elements might possess?

It must be remembered that in the days when plutonium was first discovered a group of scientists, pledged to secrecy, were examining the possibility of making an atomic bomb. The key bomb stuff was pinpointed as uranium-235, but the problem of mass-producing this material was enormously complicated and difficult. In casting about for some alternative bomb material, which would be easier to produce, they scrutinized the new elements that had just been discovered. Laboratory experiments proved that plutonium-239 fissioned under neutron bombardment just as uranium-235 did. The challenge to the scientists was this: could they mass-produce element 94? Although no one knew precisely how much plutonium would be required, even for a minimum number of bombs it would amount to hundreds of pounds.

The real answer to the challenge could be summed up quite simply: a machine producing vast numbers of neutrons was needed. Clearly, if uranium-238 could be thoroughly irradiated with neutrons, the resulting plutonium could be separated chemically from the uranium. The controlled chain reaction with which Fermi was experimenting offered the possibility of a powerful neutron source. In the preceding chapter we described the huge machines that were built near the Columbia River for the express purpose of producing plutonium.

After the war, when scientists were free to turn their full attention to the new transuranium elements, Dr. Seaborg headed up a task force at the Radiation Laboratory at Berkeley, California. This time the atom hunters decided to employ somewhat heavier ammunition in their bombardment of uranium. Using the alpha particle beam of a high-energy cyclotron, they produced a new isotope of plutonium. The reaction is:

$$_{92}U^{238} \; + \; _2He^4 \; = \; _{94}Pu^{241} \; + \; _0n^1$$
$$\text{(uranium)} \quad \text{(alpha particle)} \quad \text{(plutonium)} \quad \text{(neutron)}$$

and the Pu^{241} isotope was found to decay by beta emission with a half-life of ten years. This means that Pu^{241} jumps one place up in the Periodic System to form an isotope of element 95. In honor of the land of its birth, the new element was named americium (Am). Am^{241} was found to be fairly stable, decaying with a half-life of five hundred years. Only very minute amounts of this new element were available; special techniques had to be developed to handle such tiny quantities. The illustration shows a miniature test tube containing americium juxtaposed to the eye of a needle to give some notion of its size.

A new platform was needed for climbing higher up the Periodic System. Rather than using uranium as the starting point for their experiments, the Berkeley group selected a more advanced assault post. They took a piece of plutonium-239 and bombarded it with alpha particles, producing an isotope of mass 242 and atomic number 96. This reaction was achieved during the war, but because of secrecy the new element was not revealed until later. Element 96 was named curium (Cm) in honor of the discoverers of radium. A variety of curium isotopes have been produced; some of them are so radioactive that aqueous solutions of the element boil from the heat released through the radiations. The illustration shows how a solution of curium gives out enough light so that a photograph of it can be made in total darkness.

Element 97 was announced late in 1949; it was named

34. Photograph of a microtest tube containing a small trace of americium. A needle is shown just below the bottom of the test tube for comparison. (Courtesy Professor G. T. Seaborg)

35. A tiny amount of element 96, curium, emits light to photograph itself in a darkened room. (Courtesy Professor G. T. Seaborg)

berkelium after the city where the research was done. An isotope of americium was used as a target for high-energy alpha particles. Berkelium isotopes have been identified with half-lives ranging from four to seven thousand years.

A more massive nuclear bullet extended the discoveries beyond berkelium. A cyclotron was used to hurl ions of carbon-12, three times the weight of the alpha particle, against a target of uranium-238. Other experiments used alpha particle projectiles and a target of curium. In this way isotopes belonging to element 98 were produced. This new element was named californium (Cf); its discovery was made known in March of 1950.

The production of the next two elements beyond californium took place outside the laboratory. Traces of these elements were found in the debris from superbomb tests conducted at the U.S. Atomic Proving Grounds in the Marshall

Islands. Several hundred pounds of coral were gathered up from the site where the superbomb was exploded on November 1, 1952. This material was then chemically processed at several Atomic Energy Commission laboratories. It was hoped that some trace of elements 99 or even 100 might have been produced by the successive capture of neutrons in uranium-238. Element 99 was identified from an incredibly small sample consisting of two hundred atoms. It was named fermium (Fm) to honor Enrico Fermi. Element 100 was given the name einsteinium (E) after Albert Einstein. These discoveries brought the list of known elements to an even 100. Although scientists believed that additional elements would probably be discovered, they knew that only the smallest traces of them might be made and therefore the analytic techniques for identifying them would have to be superlative.

Ingenious experiments were devised for detecting the presence of only a few atoms. In 1955 Berkeley scientists identified element 101 on the basis of experiments in which an original sample of only one billion atoms of einsteinium had been bombarded with alpha particles. To honor the great Russian chemist Dmitri Mendeleev, the California scientists proposed that the new element be called mendelevium (Mv).

In July of 1957 still another element, number 102, was announced and dubbed nobelium (No) after Alfred Nobel and his great institute in Sweden. Still other elements will probably be discovered in the future. At the present time there are about fifty different species of new atoms lying beyond uranium. All in all, from hydrogen on up to the heaviest atom, there are about twelve hundred different nuclear species, atoms which differ from each other in some basic way. This is the great family of atoms which has grown so rapidly in the past three decades as scientists have sharpened their experimental tools and techniques.

13▪

Power from the Stars

THE billions upon billions of stars in the vast universe all have one thing in common—they are all immense masses of flaming gas. Heat evolved deep within this fiery sphere gives rise to the brilliant light which makes the star visible. Our nearest star—our sun—is the source of life on earth. Our planet is kept warm, the oceans remain unfrozen and crops grow because of solar warmth.

Our planet, earth, is but a small sphere some eight thousand miles from rim to rim. It whirls through space and, caught in the invisible grip of the sun's gravitational attraction, orbits endlessly, maintaining an average distance from the sun of 93 million miles. At this distance the earth receives only a minute fraction of the vast outpouring of heat and light that the sun radiates. In fact, two billion times more heat flies off into space than strikes the earth.

How does our sun manage to keep its heat furnaces stoked? How has it kept blazing away at this rate for five billion years? Is there any danger that it may "run out of gas"?

Only recently, with the data turned up in nuclear research, has it been possible to answer these questions. Yet from the time of the primitive caveman, the sun has been an object of

wonder and of worship. The ancients revered the Sun God
and countless humans were sacrificed on bloody altars to
assuage the fiery deity.

In more modern times wonder turned to curiosity and
curiosity to methodical investigation. Astronomers found that
the sun is a million times bigger than the earth, that the temperature at the sun's surface is about six thousand degrees
Centigrade, and that the temperature deep inside the core
must be about fifteen million degrees Centigrade. Astrophysi-
cists proved that no ordinary burning or chemical combustion could account for solar heat. They knew there was not
enough oxygen to support such a combustion. All efforts to
explain the sun's power failed; no energy source was powerful
enough to account for such flaming heat over a period of five
billion years. By all reckoning, the sun should have spent its
energy long ago; it should be a dead cinder in the sky surrounded by lifeless, frozen planets—a darkness in the universe.

Sir Arthur Eddington was the first scientist to speculate
correctly about the source of the sun's energy. He suggested
in 1920 that stars might gain energy from the combination
or fusion of hydrogen to form more complex elements. This
nuclear "burning" should release per atom a million times
more energy than any known chemical process. Eight years
later Frederic Houtermans and Robert Atkinson took the next
step which turned speculation into theory. They calculated
that hydrogen within the sun's core consisted of atoms so
speedy (due to heat and pressure) that some collisions between hydrogen atoms would produce a thermonuclear reaction with the release of heat. We call this thermonuclear
energy and, as the name implies, it is nuclear energy produced
by heat-agitated atoms.

Houtermans and Atkinson had practically no experimental
data about the behavior of hydrogen atoms, so they had to
proceed on pure theory. They knew that at the elevated temperatures inside the sun's core hydrogen atoms would be

stripped of their electrons. They also knew that the great pressure due to the overweight of the sun's voluminous mass squeezed hydrogen nuclei (protons) so close together that the result was a proton paste eight times denser than solid lead. Houtermans and Atkinson calculated that hydrogen fusion could account for solar heat. However, they could not demonstrate that the fiery proton paste in the sun's core would actually sustain a thermonuclear reaction. They lacked the vital nuclear data to predict the behavior of protons at the temperature that exists inside our sun.

At this point we must pause to show that the "temperature" and "energy" of protons or, for that matter, any particle, may be related. This is important because the nuclear behavior of a particle depends very strongly upon its energy (or its speed).

Ordinarily, temperature is easy to define. We measure the temperature of a glass of water with a household thermometer. We may measure the temperature of a glowing object such as a lamp filament or an iron poker by using an instrument that relates the color of the object and temperature. An iron poker, at room temperature, emits no light, but as it is heated to higher and higher temperatures, it changes in color from dull, barely visible red to a glowing white. We say that the poker is white-hot. Thus we measure and define the temperature of liquids and solids.

But how would you measure the temperature of a gas? At first thought, this seems easy, because we know we can glance at an outdoor thermometer and say that the temperature of the air is 80°, or whatever it happens to be. But what about the temperature of the ionized gas inside a glowing neon tube? The glass walls of the tube are cool to the touch, but inside the tube the neon atoms dash about with astonishing speed, much much faster than the closely packed molecules in a white-hot poker. And what about the temperature of protons in a beam emerging from a cyclotron? Scientists say that an ionized atom moving with a certain speed has an energy of so many electron volts. But they can also measure this in terms of temperature on a scale in which one electron volt is equiv-alent to roughly ten thousand degrees Centigrade. On this scale, a 1 Mev (million electron volt) proton has a tempera-ture equivalent of ten billion degrees Centigrade. As we shall see in the next chapter, cyclotrons easily accelerate protons to ten-million electron volts. This corresponds to protons of 100 billion degrees Centigrade, or vastly higher than the tempera-ture of the sun's innermost protons.

A Cornell University physics professor, Dr. Hans Bethe, next tackled the problem of explaining the sun's source of un-ending energy. In 1938 Bethe was in a much better position to make calculations than Houtermans and Atkinson had been a decade earlier, because experimental scientists had in the meantime come up with so much data about nuclear reac-tions. Thus Bethe was able to calculate how rapidly protons might combine with one another under conditions existing inside the sun.

Dr. Bethe developed the theory that four protons succes-sively fuse together to form a single atom of helium. This is not accomplished in one fell swoop, but is rather a multiple-stage process in which, first, two hydrogen protons collide and bind themselves together to become an atom of heavy hydro-gen, or deuterium; this fused atom of heavy hydrogen is then struck by another proton and helium-3 is formed; finally an-other proton collision results in the formation of a nucleus of helium-4. The process Bethe envisaged could take place in either of two ways, but both amounted to a synthesis or fusion of four protons, with the release of 27 Mev of energy. The energy that is released comes from the mass "lost" when the four hydrogen atoms fuse into an intimate combination which is lighter than the sum of the individual masses of the H-atoms. The mass "lost" or energy released in a single fusion is small, but because of the enormous amount of hydrogen in the sun, the process occurs frequently enough to keep the sun blazing hot. Every second about one billion tons of hydrogen undergo fusion! About one million tons of "Einstein mass" are totally converted into energy every second.

Yet this seemingly incredible amount of hydrogen is so small compared with the sun's total supply that the sun will continue to shine at its present rate for billions and billions of years before it runs out of fuel.

If we consider the heat generated per given weight of the sun rather than the total heat produced, we arrive at some rather astonishing facts. On an average, it takes five hundred tons of the sun's mass to produce one hundred watts of heat, the amount given off from a household electric lamp bulb. Even at the sun's center, where the heat is given off at a greater rate, it still takes many tons of the sun's substance to evolve one hundred watts of heat. Actually, the human body—say that of an active teen-ager—generates one hundred times more heat than is generated by an equivalent weight of hydrogen gas in the sun. The explanation is not difficult. In the first place, we are not comparing body temperature with the temperature inside the sun; but rather the rates at which each produces its heat. The sun is almost perfectly insulated by its outer layers of gas, so that even a tiny amount of heat generated at its core, though produced at a much slower rate than in the human body, is kept hot. In other words, the sun's heat is trapped inside its immense mass and leaks out to the surface very gradually. Consequently, the sun continues to build up in temperature; whereas the human body, which is poorly insulated, loses heat rather easily. Even mild exposure to wind suffices to chill a person. One way to look at the problem is to imagine a mass the size of the sun composed of people jammed together as they are in a subway—that is, matter endowed with the heat-producing capacity of an equivalent mass of people. The heat generated would be so great that after a while it would blaze up spectacularly.

The reason heat is evolved so slowly even in the center of the sun is that the hydrogen atoms are at such a low temperature. Roughly twenty million degrees Centigrade may not seem low, but from the standpoint of a nuclear reaction, the equivalent energy of the protons inside the sun's core is only 1,700 electron volts. This is a very low energy for nuclear reactions, since almost all the reactions studied with a cyclotron are measured at energies of millions of volts. Nuclear reactions, especially when we specify thermonuclear reactions, "go" faster at higher energies. This means that deep inside the sun the protons are very weak and fuse together so slowly that it takes millions of years for a hydrogen-helium cycle to occur. That is why our sun doesn't explode like a hydrogen bomb.

Hydrogen bombs release their energy in less than one-millionth of a second. The main reason why such fast reactions can be attained is that heavy and extra-heavy hydrogen are fused in the bomb reaction. Deuterium (double-weight hydrogen) and tritium (triple-weight hydrogen) react violently in contrast to the slow fusion of ordinary or single-weight hydrogen.

In their attempt to make a hydrogen bomb, the experts were up against a cost problem with regard to tritium, and thus it came as a real step ahead when they figured out a way to put a liner of lithium-6 next to the "nuke" in a bomb. The great flash of neutrons released in the explosion of the A-bomb trigger irradiates the lithium liner and gives birth to a burst of tritium atoms. The A-trigger also produces an intense heat wave.

Bomb experts killed two birds with one stone by incorporating the lithium in the form of a chemical compound called lithium deuteride, a compound formed by the synthesis of lithium and heavy hydrogen. They were thus able to bring about the fusion of deuterium and tritium. As we have seen, the fusion process releases energy—in this case, 17.6 Mev for each fusion. This is significantly less than fission energy, but we must remember that a pound of a light element like lithium contains many more atoms than a pound of a heavy element like uranium and can release more energy.

The energy released in the fusion of hydrogen comes off in the form of high-speed particles, just as in the case of fission. But there is a significant difference, for most of the energy is imparted to the neutron that is produced in the reaction. This neutron dashes off with the lion's share of the fusion energy. It is so speedy that it would tend to flash out into space and not make for a very effective bomb, if the bomb designers had not hit upon an ingenious idea.

They decided to make the runaway neutron do some work in the bomb. They put a heavy jacket of ordinary uranium around the lithium liner. The fast-flying neutrons are trapped in this jacket and there they cause the atoms of U^{238} to fission. The neutrons released in fission, you will recall, will not split U^{238} as readily as they do U^{235}. This is because U^{235} fissions with low-speed neutrons whereas U^{238} does not. Neutrons produced in the chain reaction are not in general sufficiently speedy to fission U^{238}. But, and this is most significant, the neutrons released in hydrogen fusion are fast enough to cause U^{238} to fission.

This means, then, that the superbomb is really a three-stage device. Stage one involves the firing of an atomic bomb trigger. Stage two centers upon the manufacture of tritium from lithium and the fusion of the tritium and heavy hydrogen. Stage three is the fission of ordinary uranium by the fast-fusion neutrons produced in stage two.

All these stages are interrelated by a complex neutron relationship. For example, when U^{238} fissions in stage three, the neutrons produced feed back into the bomb core, causing more fission of the A-trigger and additional production of tritium. In addition, the explosion in stage three creates more heat to produce more fusion. These reactions are so complex and all happen so fast—in one-millionth of a second—that calculation of the bomb's power is exceedingly difficult and must be relegated to whirlwind automatic computers. These electronic brains are capable of lightning-like computation and permit the bomb designers to figure out how a given weapon might perform prior to actual test.

Knowing from the reality of the H-bomb that hydrogen is useful in an explosive thermonuclear reaction, it is natural to ask if hydrogen fusion can be tamed to produce energy useful to man. Is it possible for man to imitate or outdo the sun's energy power?

Before exploring this possibility further, it will help to have clearly in mind why scientists concentrate on hydrogen as a fuel, rather than some other element. Going back to Rutherford's experiments on the scattering of alpha particles, recall that only a very few of the alpha particles penetrated close to the nucleus in the target atom. As the positively charged alpha particles sped toward the positively charged nucleus of the atom, they were strongly repelled by the like electrical forces. The same thing happens when we try to bring together two alpha particles or two hydrogen nuclei or any two nuclei. They resist fusion because of the electrical repulsion of their positively charged cores. The greater the charge on the atomic nucleus, the greater will be the repulsion and hence the difficulty of fusing the two. This means that fusion is easiest for the lighter elements; and hydrogen, with its single proton, is of course the lightest of all.

However, if man attempted to imitate nature's solar process for fusing ordinary hydrogen as fuel, he would be doomed to failure; as we saw earlier, the kind of hydrogen that is present in the sun's interior fuses very slowly, so that a single cubic inch of the central core will evolve only a fraction of a watt of heat energy. The fact of the matter is that ordinary hydrogen is too sluggish a nuclear fuel to support a controlled, man-made fusion reaction. However, as we know, other kinds of hydrogen exist: heavy hydrogen or deuterium, and the radioactive, extra-heavy form of hydrogen called tritium. Tritium or triple-weight hydrogen can be produced in a nuclear reactor by bombarding lithium with neutrons. Unlike ordinary hydrogen, deuterium and tritium react quickly to

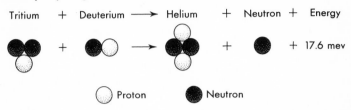

Tritium   +   Deuterium ⟶ Helium   +   Neutron +   Energy

+   17.6 mev

○ Proton   ● Neutron

36. Illustrating the fusion of two atoms of hydrogen to form a single atom of helium and a neutron.

create helium; it is this fact that will make controlled fusion power possible. These isotopes are known to undergo the following reactions:

$$_1D^2 + {_1D^2} = {_1H^1} + {_1T^3}$$
$$_1D^2 + {_1D^2} = {_2He^3} + {_0n^1}$$

$$_1D^2 + {_1T^3} = {_2He^4} + {_0n^1}$$
$$_1T^3 + {_1T^3} = {_2He^4} + {2_0n^1}$$

All these reactions release energy. The first two yield 4.13 and 3.37 Mev respectively, while the last two release 17.58 and 11.32 Mev of energy.

While the energy released by each fusion of hydrogen isotopes is considerably less than the 200 Mev for each fission of a uranium atom, as we noted earlier in the case of lithium, the number of atoms in a pound of hydrogen is very much greater than the number of atoms in a pound of uranium. A pound of deuterium, for instance, releases roughly three times as much energy as a pound of uranium. Converted into the energy content of the heavy hydrogen in a cup of water, this amounts to the heat equivalent of fifty pounds of coal. The supply of heavy hydrogen is practically without limit since the lakes and oceans on our planet contain inexhaustible reserves of water. Thus, if man can extract hydrogen fusion energy, he has at hand an unlimited new supply of fuel.

The goal of hydrogen power is tempting for more than just this reason. Hydrogen fusion produces no residual radioactive fragments, so the radiation hazard of uranium fission products is not present in this new type of power source. Furthermore, because of the nature of the reactor that will probably be used to produce fusion power, there is no danger of a runaway explosion, such as can occur in certain types of uranium power plants. In addition, there is the enticing prospect that it may be possible to derive energy from a fusion reactor directly, in the form of electrical power.

Attractive as these prospects appear, one has to consider the huge difficulties that stand in the road toward attaining fusion power. The basic fuel, deuterium, is no problem, since heavy water can be produced in hundred-ton lots and is readily available commercially at $28 per pound. And there is no problem in obtaining pure deuterium gas from the heavy water. The fundamental problem is so to design a reactor that ionized deuterium, or hydrogen plasma as it is called, can be brought to sufficiently high speed for fusion to take place. This requires that a temperature above one hundred million degrees Centigrade be attained.

Scientists in many countries are hard at work designing machines that will use electric and magnetic fields to squeeze hydrogen plasma together or "pinch" it. The basic idea was set forth in 1934 by the American physicist, W. H. Bennett. He suggested that charged particles of hydrogen moving in a stream would constitute an electrical current that should induce its own magnetic fields; this, in turn, would act to pinch the plasma together, bringing the individual ions into collision with each other. The more violent the collisions (i.e., the "hotter" the pinch) and the more frequent they are, the greater is the probability that fusion will occur.

Unfortunately, the phenomenon just described is not very

easy to control or stabilize. In the United States, the Atomic Energy Commission established Project Sherwood for the purpose of bringing about the controlled release of fusion power. The research work, begun on a modest budget in 1951, expanded to a vigorous program in 1959, backed by a forty-million-dollar annual budget. A variety of experimental devices for studying the "pinch" effect have been built at the Los Alamos Scientific Laboratory, of which the Perhapstron is an example. Hydrogen ions are circulated in a doughnut-shaped vacuum tube and constricted by an electrical current into a narrow column inside this chamber.

A "Magnetic Mirror" device represents a different approach to the fusion problem adopted by scientists at the University of California's Livermore Laboratory. Instead of a doughnut chamber, a straight tube is employed and the hydrogen plasma is "trapped" by intense magnetic fields and "reflected" back from one end of the tube into the center of the chamber. Still another line of approach is shown in the illustration. Here at Oak Ridge, scientists are studying fusion possibilities by hurling heavy hydrogen molecules downward into a reaction chamber where they are ionized by an electric arc and then subjected to intense magnetic forces. A more ambitious and larger-scale approach to fusion power is under way at Princeton University, where a Stellerator is being constructed. Magnetic forces from a thick magnetic coil that is wrapped around a figure-8-shaped vacuum chamber center the hydrogen ions in the chamber. This unusual container is designed to keep the hydrogen ions from straying out to the wall and giving up their energy. Fusion power can be attained only if the plasma can be kept isolated from contact with the container.

Obviously, no structural container can hold anything so hot as this fiery plasma. Instead, scientists propose to contain the plasma by means of magnetic fields which force the ions to stay in a restricted space, i.e., a kind of "magnetic bottle."

37. The Oak Ridge Fusion research device designed to probe hydrogen fusion on a laboratory scale. (Oak Ridge National Laboratory)

However, there is the serious problem of designing such a magnetic "container" so that it is substantially leakproof. Any small leak would allow the hot plasma to squirt out to the tube wall and cool off, thus ruining chances of attaining the high temperatures necessary for fusion. Experiments in the United States have produced plasma at a temperature of about ten million degrees Centigrade.

Fusion research is also going on in Russia, Britain, Sweden, Germany, Japan and many other countries. The British have pioneered in this new field of research and have constructed rather large machines. All machines concentrate on using deuterium as the reacting substance, although later experiments may be done with tritium. However, tritium is more difficult to handle experimentally because of the radiation hazard and the contamination of the equipment.

If one selects pure deuterium as the nuclear fuel for fusion power, there is the attractive prospect that, since two-thirds of the energy comes off in the form of charged particles, it might be possible to convert this directly into electrical energy. Picturing the way a piston functions in a steam engine, one may think of moving plasma working against magnetic fields, and electrical circuits drawing off the energy. With a mixture of deuterium and tritium, the majority of the energy is carried off by the neutrons. A blanket of liquid lithium might be used to absorb the neutrons and convert their energy into heat and at the same time generate useful tritium as the lithium atoms are fissioned. Thus fusion power would be used to produce heat external to the plasma and this heat would then be used for the purposes of producing more power.

The possibility of fusion power is raised at a time when uranium power plants are being engineered to produce power on a basis competitive with conventional fuels. Rising coal costs in England have provided the British with a strong incentive to replace coal with uranium and they have devoted tremendous effort to building uranium power stations. Now there is the question whether uranium power is not obsolete before it is even fully developed. Will not fusion of hydrogen replace uranium fission as man's source of energy? Ultimately, it seems clear that hydrogen fusion will be developed to the point where it is attractive for some applications, but this new source of power is in its technological infancy and it is too early to predict when it will assume its place in the sun. However, it can be said that many scientists who are working on this ultimate fuel are optimistic that they will be able to solve the very formidable problems that lie ahead. Furthermore, they feel that in their explorations of high-temperature plasmas and intense magnetic fields they will learn many new facts about atoms and the cosmos. Indeed, some scientists believe that even if hydrogen power should never succeed, should man be frustrated in his attempt to outdo the sun, he will gather rich dividends in fundamental knowledge, and the research will have been worth while. But the hope is that the quest for fusion power will bring to mankind an unlimited source of power to heat homes, light cities and power factories for millions of years to come.

and expression of man's fearless quest for truth."

In this quest into the remotest parts of the atom, the early atomic explorers had to proceed in a halting, uncertain manner for they had few instruments with which to probe the atom's secrets. Slowly they acquired sensitive devices to serve where the human ear or eye proved too crude an instrument. They developed electronic counters so sensitive that they respond to the passage of a single nuclear particle. They fashioned cloud chambers which reveal most graphically how the radium atom disintegrates and how nuclear collisions take place. Photographic emulsions were perfected that are sensitive enough to record the passage of ionizing radiation. Men have devoted their lives to developing special instruments to facilitate nuclear research.

Pioneers like Rutherford performed ingenious experiments using atomic projectiles available from natural radioactive sources. But such sources presented many difficulties and severely limited the experiments that could be performed. For one thing, natural radioactive sources were rather weak, giving off relatively few particles in all directions. It was necessary to screen out the majority of the particles in order to define a beam headed in one direction. One could not change the energy of these particles, so all in all the source was not very satisfactory. Scientists needed a powerful beam of charged particles which they could vary in energy and direct at will. Around 1930 some primitive machines came into existence which gave promise of providing a more versatile attack upon the stronghold of the atom. Of these the most celebrated is the cyclotron.

In the original cyclotron built by E. O. Lawrence and M. Stanley Livingston, protons were produced inside an evacuated apparatus and were boosted up to an energy of 80,000 electron volts (ev) by successive accelerations as the particles whirled round and round in a circular path. A strong magnetic field, such as can be produced in the gap between pole pieces of a

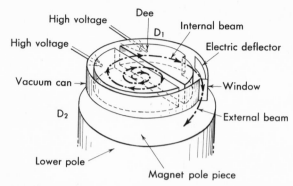

38. Sketch illustrating the principle of cyclotron acceleration. Only the lower pole face of the electromagnet is shown. Ions are produced near the center of
the vacuum chamber and follow paths as shown.

powerful electromagnet, suffices to bend electrically charged
particles in a circular orbit. This, however, was well known
and the new idea incorporated in the design of the cyclotron
was the trick of accelerating the protons every time they cir-
cled in orbit. This was accomplished by placing a split metal
can (resembling two opposed D's) inside the vacuum chamber and between the magnet's pole pieces. An alternating
voltage was imposed on this split can in a way that gave an
electrical push to the protons as they entered the can between
the D's. Neat timing was required for this feat since the protons took very little time to complete a half-circle and when
this time elapsed the voltage on the opposite dee (D) had
to attract the protons. This stunt was accomplished by applying a high-frequency (rapidly oscillating) voltage to the dees.
The method was so successful that ions of heavy hydrogen
were boosted to an energy of 60 million electron volts (Mev)
in a cyclotron constructed in the late 1930s on the campus
of the University of California. The powerful atom-smashing
beam is shown emerging from the cyclotron in the illustration.
Note that the beam that is made visible by ionization of the
air proceeds in a straight-line path once it leaves the cyclotron;

39. The 60-Mev deuteron beam of the University of California 60-inch cyclotron is shown emerging from the accelerator. (University of California)

this is because the charged particles are deflected from their circular paths and then, free of the restraining influence of the magnetic field, shoot off in a straight line like drops of water spun off a rapidly rotating wheel.

Physicists were able to use the powerful beam from the 60-inch cyclotron (such machines are classified in terms of the diameter of their magnet pole pieces) for investigating nuclear reactions in many elements. Furthermore, it was relatively easy to change the energy of the beam so that quantitative information could be obtained on the behavior of swiftly moving, charged particles and their interactions with atoms. As we know, many new radioactive species of atoms were discovered; in addition it was found that some of these could be manufactured in cyclotron bombardments and then used in medical and biological research. As a matter of fact, a number of cyclotrons were built specifically for the production of radioisotopes.

However, the principal interest of the physicist in acquiring more energetic particles was the investigation of the internal make-up or structure of the nucleus. What was the nature of the internal glue that held the nucleus together? How far out from the nucleus did this nuclear force extend? What other particle existed in the nucleus in addition to the well-known neutron and proton?

Nuclear physicists were not proceeding completely in the dark, because investigations in cosmic ray research had turned up some fascinating phenomena about subnuclear particles. Cosmic rays are very energetic, electrically charged particles that zoom in from space and bombard the earth constantly. We know now that the majority of these rays are protons, most of which have energy measured in the billions of electron volts. It is still not clear where these speedy space travelers originate, but we know a great deal about their behavior once they spiral into the earth's atmosphere. Ingenious experiments have been performed using Geiger counters arranged in clever combinations so as to form a "cosmic ray telescope"; these devices have been taken up to mountain tops to measure the cosmic radiation. Cloud chambers were also used to snap pictures of the elusive cosmic particles, and because such photographs, taken at random, would trap very few cosmic rays or "catch them in the act," sets of Geiger counters were placed above and below the cloud chamber and electronically rigged so that a cosmic ray penetrating both sets of counters would automatically operate the cloud chamber. Thus cosmic rays were made to trigger the apparatus and take their own pictures.

Striking photographs have thus been made that reveal much about the nature of the cosmic rays. In the accompanying photograph we see a thin track which curves through the chamber under the influence of a magnet placed around the chamber. Note that when the ionizing particle strikes the aluminum plate inside the chamber, it emerges on the other

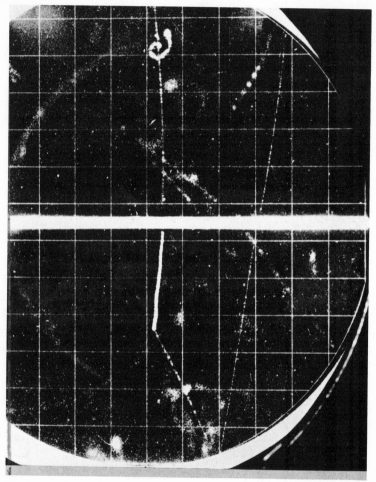

40. A cosmic ray meson enters the top of the chamber, traverses a quarter-inch-thick aluminum plate and stops in the chamber gas, emitting an electron. (R. W. Thompson)

side with less energy, as is shown by the fact that it is bent more sharply by the magnetic field. Note also that in the lower half of the picture the track of the particle thickens, i.e., the particle becomes more ionizing as it reaches the end of its path. Then something quite spectacular happens; the particle stops in the gas inside the chamber and gives birth to another particle, as is evidenced by the light track which juts out from the line of the flight of the original particle. Physicists have techniques for estimating the mass of a particle from its ionization and curvature inside a cloud chamber. The mass of the cosmic ray passing through the aluminum plate is estimated as several hundred times that of an electron; such a particle is called a meson. The particle produced when this meson comes to rest in the chamber is an electron. In short, the cosmic ray meson slows down and is stopped in the chamber gas; as it comes to the end of its life, it spontaneously disintegrates and emits an electron.

The meson, which was first identified in cosmic ray research, did not come upon the scene without any advance notice. Far from it; in 1935 the brilliant Japanese theoretician, Hidekei Yukawa, predicted that such a particle of mass intermediate between that of an electron and a proton ought to exist. Yukawa looked upon this particle, which we now call the meson, as responsible for binding together the neutron and proton inside a nucleus. It was, according to Yukawa's theory, an "exchange" particle which both the neutron and proton shared. In other words, he was accounting for the cohesion of nuclei by assuming that protons and neutrons constantly exchange a charged meson; thus a neutron transforms itself into a proton and back again billions of times every second. The exchange of the meson acts as a binding force between the two particles. It was a revolutionary concept of "nuclear glue." The meson, if it could be freed from its intimate association with nuclear particles, would have a transitory life and die within a split millionth of a second.

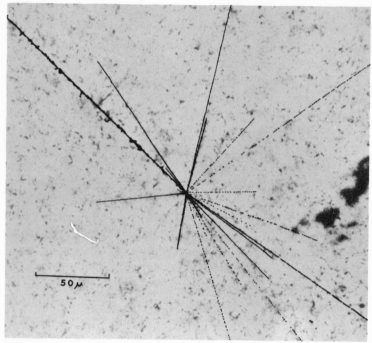

41. A heavy primary cosmic ray smashes into a nucleus and produces a spectacular explosion, blasting nuclear fragments in all directions. The photograph is an enlargement of a photographic emulsion sent up into the stratosphere in an unmanned balloon. Research of this type probes deep into the heart of the nucleus. (Courtesy H. Yagoda, National Institutes of Health)

An even more revealing picture of the meson is given by the fleeting impression of the charged particles as they streak through a bit of photographic emulsion carried up into the stratosphere by unmanned balloons. British scientists developed specially sensitive photographic emulsions and sent packs of them aloft in these free-floating clusters of balloons. Sometimes the balloons soared twenty miles or more up in the rarefied atmosphere, where the cosmic rays are more abundant. As a result of such lofty experiments, the British physicists discovered that there are, in fact, two kinds of

mesons. They identified a heavy species which they called the pi-meson; this is very unstable and decays in a lifetime of a quarter-billionth of one second. The pi-meson decays into a light or mu-meson. The heavy meson weighs 273 times more than an electron, whereas the mu-meson is 206 times the mass of an electron.

These exciting discoveries of the British researchers spurred U.S. scientists at the Berkeley Radiation Laboratory to intensify their efforts in building a bigger atom-smasher. They dreamed that if they could hurl particles to very high energy they might create mesons in the laboratory. Actually, the push toward high energy was started before the war, but the work had to be abandoned in favor of atomic weapon research. Dr. E. O. Lawrence had constructed a huge electromagnet with pole faces 184 inches in diameter. With this he hoped to zip ions up to 100 million electron volts of energy. He knew, however, that what he was attempting to do in this supercyclotron was almost impossible. To understand the problem that perplexed the machine designers, we must understand a little more about the behavior of nuclear particles at high energy. It is fundamental to Einstein's theory that as particles approach the velocity of light they must inevitably increase in mass. That this is true has been verified experimentally; for example, electrons accelerated to 100,000 volts in, say, an X-ray tube weigh 20 per cent more than when at rest. Some hospitals and institutes have million-volt X-ray installations; in these devices electrons actually double in mass owing to this Einstein effect.

We have already noted that in the operation of a cyclotron it is imperative that the ions that circulate inside the vacuum chamber must arrive at the dee gap at precisely the right moment if they are to be accelerated by the voltage applied to the dee. As the ions go faster and faster, they tend to increase in mass and therefore they take longer to complete an orbit within the dees. The result is that these sluggish ions

tend to lag behind the applied voltage or, so to speak, they get out of step and fail to receive the proper acceleration. Thus it appeared that the Einstein effect would forever limit the machine builders to 100 Mev or so in energy. The Einstein barrier seemed to be an impenetrable obstacle to the cyclotron designers.

Two scientists, Edwin McMillan in the United States and V. Veksler in Russia, independently hit upon the idea for getting around this barrier. Nothing could be done to prevent the particles from increasing in mass, but it was found possible to redesign the big machine so that the electric and magnetic fields were synchronized. By programming the electric and magnetic fields, it is possible to keep the ions constantly accelerated. The original 184-inch Berkeley machine was finally redesigned so that it produced a beam of 380 Mev alpha particles. And in 1948 scientists at Berkeley succeeded in producing mesons artificially.

The artificial production of mesons proved to be only the beginning of a series of sensational discoveries with high-energy particles. One thing that impressed physicists was the fact that nuclear particles have their opposite numbers. For example, the ordinary or negative electron has its anti-partner, the positron, and the negatively charged meson has a positively charged opposite number. In like manner, scientists felt that there must exist an anti-proton, having the same mass as the proton but an opposite electrical charge. They reckoned this particle could be observed if enough energy were available to create a pair of protons—one, the ordinary proton or core of the simple H atom, and the other, the unfound anti-proton. They estimated that they would have to accelerate the bombarding projectiles in a big machine until they reached 4.5 billion electron volts (Bev) in order to create this proton pair.

Practical considerations dictated that such a Bev accelerator would have to be of a design different from that of the 184-inch synchrocyclotron. It would require battleship quantities of magnet iron in order to make an electromagnet with pole faces large enough to accommodate the great circular path of high-energy protons. Therefore the designers replaced the conventional yoke-type magnet with a ring-shaped wrap-around magnet 100 feet in diameter. With this synchrotron, bunches of ten billion protons were boosted up to 6 Bev, traveling some 300,000 miles in the process, from start to finish.

In the fall of 1955, a team of California researchers succeeded in their hunt for the strange new particle, the anti-proton. Finding it was like hunting for a needle in a haystack, because the six-billion volt protons created intense sprays of mesons. The mesons confused the issue, acting as a smoke screen to conceal the presence of the occasional anti-protons. An ingenious combination of magnetic sorting devices was developed that blocked most of the mesons and allowed the anti-protons to shoot through; in this way the elusive anti-proton was discovered.

Just as an electron and a positron lunge together in a death grip that results in the annihilation of both partners, so, too, do the proton and the anti-proton annihilate each other in a convulsive collision. The death of an anti-proton is often a spectacular explosion, as may be seen from the myriad particles shot out of a nucleus (parent to the proton hit by the anti-proton) in the photograph.

Physicists are now striving for higher energies, seeking to duplicate cosmic ray energies here on earth. An immense proton synchrotron is being built on Long Island at the Brookhaven National Laboratory. Protons will orbit in a vacuum chamber that nests inside a magnet 840 feet in diameter. The huge magnet is buried inside a concrete tunnel. Protons boosted to 50 Mev by a separate accelerator will be squirted into orbit and then hurled up to an energy of between 25 and 30 Bev. This machine will top the performance of the 10 Bev accelerator now operating in the Soviet Union. The race to higher and higher energies seems limited largely by economic

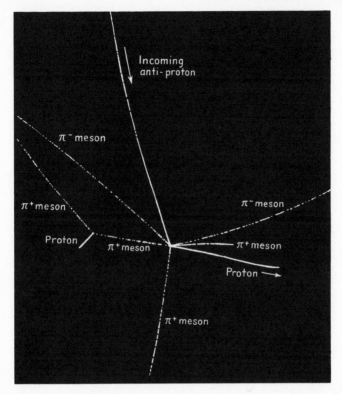

42. A bubble chamber photograph of an anti-proton streaking in from the top and colliding with a nucleus to produce a spray of particles. The dense track moving off to the right is probably a proton, while the other particles are positive and negative pi-mesons. The collision of the anti-proton with a carbon nucleus results in its annihilation. (University of California, Radiation Laboratory)

considerations; the cost of constructing the big machines is measured in the tens of millions of dollars. One huge accelerator recently proposed in the United States would cost $100 million. Obviously, if such funds are to be made available for pure scientific research, the Congress and the public which pays the bill must decide upon the value of nuclear research to the nation's future well-being. It is hard to argue that these big machines will promote the public welfare by adding to

our store of fundamental knowledge, because the nature of
the research is so far from the public understanding. Given
the alternative of voting for something concrete like a dam,
the average Congressman today may see little reason to ap-
prove funds for a machine which may never produce any
practical results.

One of the biggest obstacles to Congressional and public
understanding of science (as opposed to technology) is the
strange nature of the subatomic world of the modern scientist.
The language of the nuclear physicist is most unclear to the
man in the street. Such fundamental particles as the meson
are Greek to the nonscientist. Yet the gap between the scientist and the nonscientist must be closed, and education is
the only means to accomplish this feat. The scientist must
help by climbing down from his ivory tower and the citizen
must co-operate by trying to learn something about the nature
of the new world in which we all live.

Many people shudder at the prospect of communing with
science or the scientist. They have a concept of science as a
cold, mechanical affair, and regard the scientist as a feeling-
less robot. Or they believe that the scientist is exclusively a
weapons maker. They fail to sense that science is truly the
great adventure of the twentieth century—the culmination
of man's long struggle to free himself from want and to en-
noble himself with the inspiring knowledge of the grandeur
of the universe—or, to use Henry Huxley's expression, "the
infinitely great and the infinitely small between which our
little race of life is run."

Man, having probed the depths of the atom, is now reaching out from his earthly prison to untangle the mysteries of
other planets, of the sun and even of other stars. His audacity
is unlimited as he seeks to surmount the earth-binding force
of gravity and arc into space on missions of novel exploration.
And in so doing he will probe into the mystery of life itself.
His vision is clearing in this respect; he no longer puts him-

self in a unique position at the center of the universe. Indeed, he even dreams of other worlds, of a million planets, and of another earth on which intelligent life exists. Given such a magnificent view of the cosmos, it is not unreasonable to suppose that somewhere in the vastness of space there are colonies whose civilizations are a million years in advance of ours.

The brain is numbed by the mere thought of what science will accomplish in a million years; it is difficult to project even a decade ahead in time. No one predicted Einstein's theory or the splitting of the atom. Equally momentous developments lie ahead of us in the great territory which now comes within view. Science is truly the great adventure and scientists are the great explorers of the unknown.

Index